KEY SKILLS
LEVEL 3

Survival

Key
Skills

Level 3

Application of Number

Author
Judith Heywood

Contents

An introduction to Key Skills

Key Skills are...

Generic skills that help to improve learning and performance in:

★ Education and training　　★ Work and life in general

They are important in:

★ learning　　★ career and　　★ personal life

Key Skills aim to...

Develop and recognise skills in:

- obtaining and interpreting different types of information
- using, developing and communicating information to meet the purpose of studies, work and other activities
- effectively presenting results

Curriculum 2000

From September 2000, if you are a Curriculum 2000 student, you will be aiming to achieve Key Skills units alongside your main programme of study. Just like any other subject, Key Skills need to be taught and developed before you can produce successful final evidence.

Key Skills will play an important part in widening your studies and experiences along with other initiatives, such as community service or any other 'enhancement' studies. You could also consider any full-time or part-time employment you have which could give you the opportunity to develop and evidence some of your skills.

You will be using many of the skills already without even realising it. Take a look at Appendix E (page 78) where you will see the list of qualifications that you may already have and that could give you exemption(s) from some parts of the Key Skills Awards. (Make sure you ask your teachers for an up-to-date list. This one was current in June 2000.)

From 2000 onwards, many students will also use the opportunities presented by their Citizenship studies to develop and evidence their Key Skills. Every qualification you study from September 2000 will be sign-posted for its opportunities for Key Skills development and evidence.

HE, Key Skills and the world of work

- Higher Education institutions are working on developing the Key Skills of their students in order to make them more autonomous and effective learners.

- The points that will be awarded by UCAS for applicants for HE in September 2002 for each of the Key Skills (Communication, Application of Number and IT) will be as follows:

Level	UCAS points per unit
Level 4	30 points
Level 3	20 points
Level 2	10 points

(To see the specifications for Level 2 and Level 4 you can visit the QCA website on www.qca.org.uk)

- Key Skills will also form an integral part of the curriculum for the new Foundation Degrees which will be launched in September 2001. These degrees will be designed to build on the breadth of study and Key Skills that you gain from Curriculum 2000.

- Employers have always loved Key Skills. They may not have called them that, but they constantly ask for people who can work both in a team and on their own. They want people who can quickly synthesise information and present it in an appropriate form. They like employees who are accurate with numbers and can use IT to enhance the content and presentation of their work.

'Key Skills are skills that are commonly needed for success in a range of activities in education and training, work and life in general. The Key Skills units aim to develop and recognise candidates' ability to apply these skills in ways that are appropriate to different contexts in order to improve the quality of learning and performance. They are intended for everyone, from pupils in school to chief executives in large companies.'
Guidance on the Key Skills Units, QCA (2000)

The individual Key Skills

From September 2000, new Key Skills will be launched. There are six Key Skills:

- **Communication (C)**
- **Information Technology (IT)**
- **Application of Number (N)**
- **Working with Others (WO)**
- **Improving own Learning and Performance (LP)**
- **Problem Solving (PS)**

- The first three are often known as the 'hard' or main Key Skills and the last three as the 'soft' or 'wider' Key Skills. This book will concentrate, along with the other two volumes in this series, on developing your 'hard' Key Skills. These are the three that will attract UCAS points.

- Each Key Skill has separate units up to and including Level 4. All the units for each level are presented in the same way. Level 5 is assessed by way of one single integrated unit.

Key Skills levels

Level 1	A student working at this level might be in the first year of a GCSE course or might achieve a D-G at GCSE.
Level 2	A student who is capable and able to gain A*-C at GCSE should be working at this level.
Level 3	Students working towards A/S, A Level and GNVQ/Vocational A Levels should be capable of this level in some or all of the Key Skills.
Level 4	Students working at undergraduate level should be developing skills at this level in some or all Key Skills.
Level 5	This is a managerial, postgraduate level and is gained by putting together a large body of evidence to demonstrate application of these high level skills. Note: generally you would need to be in a role/job that would allow you to demonstrate competence at this level, i.e. managerial or supervisory.

Not everyone will be at the same level in every Key Skill or wish to progress to the same level. You may feel that you will not need to achieve Level 3 in Application of Number to follow your career goal or you may find that IT at Level 2 is sufficient at the moment. Key Skills awards allow you to achieve at the level most appropriate for **you**, while giving you the chance to develop. It is always possible to pick up your Key Skills at a later stage and develop them further. **You should also bear in mind that some students will have chosen subject combinations at post-16 that give them more opportunities for Key Skills developments than others.**

It doesn't matter which awarding/examining body your school or college uses, as all the requirements for achieving your Key Skills are identical. Institutions may use the same awarding body, which will accredit your other qualifications, or they may choose one awarding body to accredit all their Key Skills candidates.

Where will my Key Skills evidence come from?

Your teachers and tutors will be working to make Key Skills attainments as straightforward as possible for you. A great deal of your evidence for the individual units will come from work that you undertake for your other subjects. You will also find that one piece of work can cover the requirements of more than one Key Skill, for example one essay may cover elements of Communication, IT, Working with Others and Problem Solving. It is important that you get to grips with the Unit Specifications – if you understand them well you can plan to get the maximum Key Skills material from each piece of work. In this way you will be gaining extra qualifications without giving yourself a great deal of extra work.

How are Key Skills assessed?

There are two elements to the assessment of Key Skills.

1. A **portfolio** of naturally occurring evidence which will be:

- **internally assessed** (by your tutors/teachers)
- **internally verified/moderated** (teachers check each others' marks to make sure they are all working to the same standards)
- **externally moderated** (by a representative from the awarding body to assure that all internal marking is to the standard required)

2. An **external assessment instrument** to assess:

- **knowledge/understanding**
- **externally set tasks**

You have to pass both of these elements in order to achieve your Key Skills unit(s). The Unit Specifications tell you everything you need to know in order to do this.

The Key Skills Qualification

Every Key Skill is available in its own right as a free-standing unit. But those students who achieve the **three** Key Skills – **Application of Number, Communication and Information Technology** – will receive a national certificate of units **and** the Key Skills Qualification.

It doesn't matter at what level you get the Key Skills, as they will be profiled, for example two at Level 3 and one at Level 2.

The Key Skills Qualification is a profile of achievement in three Key Skills units:

Portfolio and Test =
COMMUNICATION
+
Portfolio and Test =
APPLICATION OF NUMBER
+
Portfolio and Test =
INFORMATION TECHNOLOGY

Considering the wider Key Skills

The specifications for the three 'wider' Key Skills – **Working With Others (WO)**, **Improving Own Learning and Performance (LP)** and **Problem Solving (PS)** – are important to the worlds of study and employment, and for your personal development.

Your school or college may or may not enter students for the wider Key Skills: this does not mean that you should ignore them. Even if you are not aiming for a formal qualification in the wider Key Skills, you will find that you will benefit personally and academically if you aim to develop these skills and gain unit certification.

Working With Others (WO)

In school, college or in part-time employment, are there situations where you have to:

- agree objectives, who does what, when and how?
- organise your time and tasks in order to achieve what you have agreed?
- work co-operatively with others (even if you don't like them!)?
- review what you are doing and consider whether better ways of working can be devised?

Improving Own Learning and Performance (LP)

In school, college or part-time employment, are there situations where you have to:

- identify and agree targets and action plans yourself to meet these targets?
- follow your action plan and gain support and feedback from others when necessary to enable you to meet your targets?
- realistically review and assess your progress and provide evidence of this progress and your achievements?

Problem Solving (PS)

In school, college or part-time employment, do you ever have to:

- identify, consider and describe problems?
- identify and compare different ways in which you could solve problems?
- plan and put into place a solution?
- devise, agree and apply methods for checking that a problem has been solved and review approaches to tackling problems?

If you can say 'Yes' to any of these, have a close look at the Unit Specifications for the wider Key Skills at Level 3. You probably already have the potential to produce evidence that meets the specifications.

(For more details on the wider Key Skills, visit the QCA website at www.qca.org.uk)

What you need to know – Application of Number Level 3

This book will help you to achieve Key Skill Application of Number at Level 3.

In Chapters 4 and 5 you will find practice material to help you pass the Key Skills Application of Number test. Chapters 6 to 9 contain help on how to build your portfolio.

Key Skills levels

> To gain Key Skill Unit Certification in Application of Number at Level 3, you need to pass a test of your skills and knowledge (Part A) and build a portfolio of evidence (Part B/C) to demonstrate your ability in applying these skills.

If you are aiming for Level 3 in Application of Number, it is assumed that you already have the skills required at Levels 1 and 2.

Look at the outlines for the requirements at each Key Skill level for Application of Number. Compare what is expected at each level. At which level do you feel most confident?

Level 1	Level 2	Level 3
You must be able to: <ul><li>interpret straightforward information</li><li>carry out calculations using whole numbers, simple decimals, fractions and percentages to a given level of accuracy</li><li>interpret the results of your calculations and present your findings using a chart and a diagram</li></ul>	You must be able to carry through a substantial and straightforward activity that requires you to: <ul><li>select information and methods to get the results you need</li><li>carry out calculations involving two or more steps and numbers of any size, including the use of formulae, and check your methods and levels of accuracy</li><li>select ways to present your findings, including the use of a graph, describe methods and explain results</li></ul>	You must be able to plan and carry through a substantial and complex activity that requires you to: <ul><li>plan your approach to obtain and use information, choose appropriate methods to obtain results and justify your choice</li><li>carry out multi-stage calculations, including use of a large data set (over 50 items) and rearrangement of formulae</li><li>justify your choice of presentation methods and explain the results of your calculations</li></ul>

> If you have not already seen a Key Skills specification, you will find the full specification for Application of Number Level 3 printed in Appendix A on pages 66–69.

What level should you be aiming for?

Many students studying AS/A Level and Vocational A Level courses will be aiming for Level 3 in their Key Skills. Some courses offer more opportunities than others to practise applying your number skills. However, students will benefit from developing these skills and it is possible to achieve your Key Skills at the most appropriate level for you. The Key Skills Qualification is a profiled award. A student's level of achievement will be recorded and may vary from one Key Skill to another.

REMEMBER...

You should try to develop your number skills as far as you can. Everyone needs to be able to deal confidently with aspects of life such as income tax, finding the best deal for a mobile phone or a cheap foreign holiday, and how to manage personal finances while at College or University.

- If you feel confident with Maths and know all you need is a little practice to brush up your skills, then you should aim for Level 3.

- If you only just passed Maths GCSE and find Maths problems hard, then aim for Level 2. With a C grade at Maths GCSE, you will be exempt from the Level 2 Number test. (See Appendix E on pages 78-79 for a list of qualifications giving exemption from Key Skills assessments.)

- Even if you do not feel confident to go for Level 3, if you have already secured a grade C pass at Maths GCSE and you complete a Level 2 Application of Number portfolio, you will be able to gain a Key Skill in Application of Number at Level 2, which is worth 10 UCAS points.

The external assessment

Part A of Application of Number Level 3 is an external assessment. In other words, it is a test of your application of number in a range of contexts.

What sort of test will I take?

The tests are different at Levels 2 and 3.

- The test at Level 2 is a non-calculator paper that takes an hour and consists of 40 multiple choice questions. It aims to test your competence in basic number skills.

- At Level 3, the test paper consists of questions requiring a mixture of long and short answers, each set in a number context. The test is $1\frac{1}{2}$ hours long and you are allowed to use a calculator.

If you achieved a grade C or above at Maths GCSE with ease, it is likely you will cope well with the level of skills required for Level 3. On the other hand, if you just scraped a grade C in Maths, you will need to work hard on improving these skills. Whatever your ability, if you brush up your number skills using the practice questions given in Chapter 4, you should have a better chance of passing the Level 3 test, where the emphasis is on 'application'. Detailed answers are given in Appendix B (pages 70-74).

PROXY QUALIFICATIONS

> **Some qualifications, which you may already have achieved or be working towards, give exemption from parts of some Key Skills. There is a list of these in Appendix E (page 78). (This was accurate as of June 2000.)**
>
> **If you think you may be entitled to any exemption, get your tutor to check for you.**

What will I be tested on?

Part A of the Unit Specification tells you what knowledge and skills you will be tested on. It is divided into three sections:

- planning and obtaining information

- carrying out calculations

- interpreting results and presenting findings

Read through the Unit Specification (see pages 66-69) and make sure you understand what you need to know. The End Test will not cover all of these skills, but you must feel confident enough to tackle whatever is on the paper.

Skills and knowledge tested at Level 3

Read through Part A of the Unit Specification again (see Appendix A, page 67). The skills and techniques that are required for Part A of Level 3 are summarised below.

- **Addition, subtraction, multiplication and division of all types of number;** confident use of decimals, fractions, ratios and percentages; understanding equivalencies ($40\% = \frac{2}{5}$); positive and negative numbers.

- **Estimating and rounding** to an appropriate level of accuracy, e.g. to 2 decimal places.

- **Multiplying and dividing numbers of any size.**

- **Using numbers in the form £2.3 million, standard form (2.4×10^{-3}) and compound form** (speed in mph, kph).

- Use of **ratio and scales**, such as 1:1250, to work out measurements; sharing to a given ratio.

- **Conversion of currencies and measurements;** knowledge of well-known equivalencies, e.g. 2.54 cm = 1 inch.

- Using **percentages** to find VAT; interest on investments over 5 years; % change.

- **Rearranging and using formulae**: equations; substituting values; use of powers and roots to find areas and volumes; solving simultaneous linear equations with two variables.

- Using **Pythagoras' Theorem and basic trigonometric** identities for tan, sin and cosine to find missing angles and sides in right-angled triangles.

- Using **checking procedures**: doing reverse calculations; making sure answers make sense; checking by estimating what an answer should be.

- Using **data collection techniques**: planning; surveys; tabulating and grouping data; use of suitable techniques to ensure representative, unbiased and random sampling.

- The application and interpretation of suitable **statistical calculations for mean, median, mode and range** for grouped and ungrouped data.

- The accurate construction and interpretation of display methods such as **graphs, diagrams, scale drawings, charts.**

This list may seem daunting. Do not be defeated. It is amazing how much you know when you really start working. You just need to wake up those brain cells.

Basic formulae

Learn these – they are not given in the test.

Area of a rectangle = Length × Width

Area of a triangle = $\frac{1}{2}$ × Base × Height

Volume of a cuboid = Length × Width × Height

Volume of a prism = Area of cross section × Length

Area of a circle = π × Radius^2

Circumference of a circle = π × Diameter

Perimeter = distance all around an object

Pythagoras' Theorem: If **a** is the length of the hypotenuse, and **b** and **c** are the lengths of the other two sides of a right-angled triangle, then $\mathbf{a}^2 = \mathbf{b}^2 + \mathbf{c}^2$ or $\mathbf{a} = \sqrt{[\mathbf{b}^2 + \mathbf{c}^2]}$

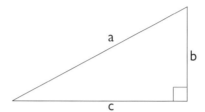

Trigonometric Ratios:

tan θ = opposite/adjacent

sin θ = opposite/hypotenuse

cos θ = adjacent/hypotenuse

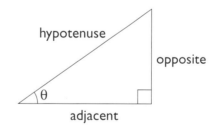

The **arithmetic mean** is the average value.

The **median** is defined as the middle value in a frequency distribution.

The **mode** is the value with the highest frequency.

The **range** is the difference between the highest and lowest values.

External assessment practice questions

BRUSH UP YOUR NUMBER SKILLS!

First work through Part I. These questions aim to help you brush up your number skills. Then try the questions in Part II to apply these skills. The questions are in the same style as the Key Skills Level 3 test. Answers for all questions are in Appendix B on pages 70-74.

Part I – Questions to practise number skills

Do not use a calculator for these questions.

Basic use of number, fractions, decimals, ratio and percentages

1   Ian sees an advert for a job in a newspaper. This is how the advert begins:

> Computer Service Technician
>
> Salary £26K

Find the monthly salary for the job.

2   There are 72 cars in the swimming pool car park. $\frac{2}{3}$ of the cars are over three years old. How many are over three years old?

3   Andrew spends $\frac{1}{2}$ of his weekly income on food, $\frac{1}{8}$ on entertainment and $\frac{1}{4}$ on clothes. He saves the remainder. How much does he save?

4   In a local election, $\frac{4}{15}$ of the electorate voted Conservative, $\frac{3}{5}$ voted Labour and the remainder voted Liberal Democrat.

a)   What fraction of the electorate voted Liberal Democrat?

b) If the number voting Conservative was 1500, find the total number who voted in the election.

5   A club has 260 members. 55% are girls. How many girls belong to the club?

6   An antique chair is bought for £50 and sold for £65. Calculate the percentage profit.

7   A field has a population of 40 rabbits. After a year the population has increased by 5%. How big is the population at the end of the year.

8   A printer is priced at £70 plus VAT. Calculate the VAT at 17.5% on the price.

9   Richard is mixing paints using pink, mauve and blue colours in the ratio of 10:5:1. He uses 3.5 litres of mauve paint. How much pink paint will he use?

10 Ben, Steven and Anthony have shares in a boat in the ratio of 5:2:3. They want to work out how much time they can each spend on the boat over a period of 100 days. Calculate how many days each of them can have.

11 Hannah earns £280 per week and Claire earns £140 per week. Find, in its simplest form, the ratio of their weekly earnings.

Formulae, use of powers, area and volume

12 The cost of hiring a van is £25 plus 25p for every mile travelled.

a) Calculate the cost of hiring the van and driving 300 miles.

b) How many miles will you have travelled if the total hire charge is £150?

c) Write a formula for the cost of hiring the car when you have driven 'x' miles.

13 Using the formula Speed = Distance/Time

a) Find the speed of a car driven 90 miles in $1\frac{1}{2}$ hours.

b) Rearrange the formula to find one for distance.

c) Find the distance travelled for a journey of $2\frac{1}{2}$ hours at a speed of 80 mph.

14

On a particular day, the formula for changing pounds sterling to Spanish pesetas is

P = £ × 242

Where £ is the number of pounds and P is the number of pesetas.

a) Martin is going to Spain and wants to change £150 to pesetas. How many pesetas does he get?

b) What is the formula for changing pesetas to £ sterling?

15 A circle has a radius of 10 cm. Using $\pi = 3.14$, find

a) the area of the circle

b) the circumference of the circle

Negative numbers, large numbers, rounding and standard form

16 Eric has an overdraft of £45 in his bank account and pays in £100. How much is his bank balance now?

17 The temperature in Helsinki was 6 °C at noon and then fell by 21 °C at midnight. How many degrees was the temperature at midnight?

18 Supersave sold £43.7 millions of baked beans, £25.2 millions of tinned pineapple and £63.5 millions of breakfast cereal over a period of six months.

a) Calculate the total sales of these three items and write the number fully in figures.

b) Give the approximate value of these sales to 2 significant figures.

19 a) Write in words the number 60,254,300.

b) Write the number in part a) in standard form to 3 significant figures.

c) Write in figures the number three million, twenty thousand and forty-two.

d) Write the number in part c) to the nearest thousand.

20 a) The population of Horsham is 43,000. Write this number in standard form.

b) The population of Great Britain is approximately 58,123,000. Express this number in standard form to 2 significant figures.

c) The coefficient of expansion for steel is 0.000012. Express this number in standard form.

d) Write 2.48×10^6 as a number.

e) Write 2.48×10^{-6} as a number.

Plans and scales, more area and volume

21 The diagram shows the plan of a living room.

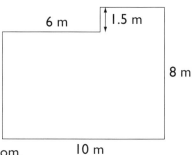

a) Calculate the total floor area of the living room.

b) Calculate the total perimeter.

c) Calculate the total volume, if the height is 2.3 m.

d) A plan of the room is made, drawn to scale, using a scale of 1m = 2.3 cm. How long is the room on the plan in centimetres?

22 A barrel of ale is approximately cylindrical in shape. It measures 50 cm long and the circular base has a radius of 10 cm. Using the conversion 1000 cm^3 = 1 litre, find the volume of ale in litres that the barrel can contain.

Mean, median, mode and range

23 Nine children are given varying amounts of pocket money: £10.20, £6.80, £4.80, £5.60, £10.50, £7.50, £7.50, £9.30 and £9.80. Use these values to find the mean, median, mode and range.

Use of equations

24 An ice cream seller charges Shima £5.90 for 4 cones and 3 choc-ices. He charges another customer £4.30 for 2 cones and 3 choc-ices. Find the price of 1 cone and the price of 1 choc-ice.

25 The ages of a man and his son total 48. In 4 years' time the father will be seven times older than his son. How old are they both now?

26 Daryl has won a prize of £150 in a competition. He wants to buy videotapes and CDs with his winnings. He expects to pay £10 for CDs and £6 for tapes. He can store up to 12 CDs and up to 9 tapes.

   a) Write three inequalities for the information given.

   b) Draw a graph of your inequalities.

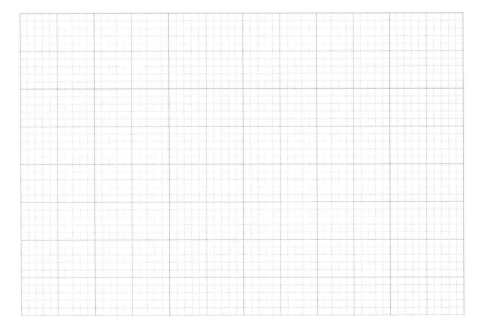

   c) What would you advise Daryl to buy? Give a reason.

Trigonometry and Pythagoras

You will need to use a calculator for the rest of the questions in part 1.

27

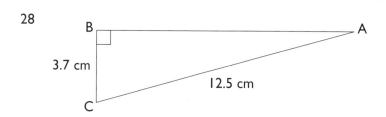

Find the length of AC. (Hint: use Pythagoras)

28

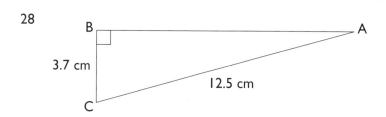

Find the length of AB. (Hint: use Pythagoras)

29

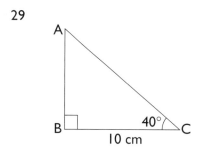

Find length AB. (Hint: now use trigonometry)

30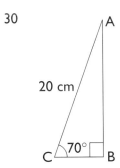

Find length BC.

31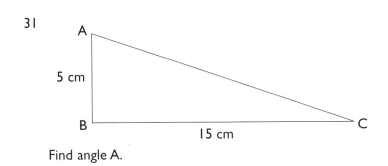

Find angle A.

Part II – Longer questions for Level 3 practice

You can use a calculator for these questions. You are allowed to use an ordinary scientific calculator for the Level 3 test, but not a graphical calculator.

1   In a sale, all goods are reduced by 15%. A vacuum cleaner costs £170 in the sale. Calculate the original price of the vacuum cleaner.

2
> Police sources claim that burglaries in one region will fall by 10% each year.
>
> In 1996, there were 4,500 reported burglaries.

   a)   If this trend continues, calculate the number of burglaries predicted for 1997.

   b)   How many will there be at the end of the year 2000, if this trend continues?

3
> This is Sonal's recipe for fruit pudding. It makes enough for 6 people.
>
> 150 g of sugar   120 g margarine
> 180 g of self-raising flour   240 g of mixed fruit

   Sonal wants to make a fruit pudding for 15 people.

   a)   How much mixed fruit does she need?

   b)   Work out how much flour she needs.

4   This is a plan for a house and garden.

    scale 1 cm = 2.5 m

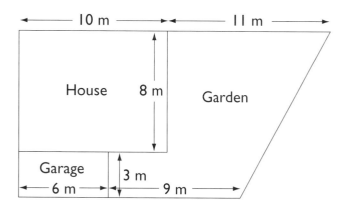

a) Find the area of the garden.

b) The house has patio doors, which are 3.65 m wide. Find how long the doors
    will measure on the plan.

5   A cereal packet measures 7.5 cm by 16 cm and is 30.5 cm tall. A factory machine
    is set to fill the packet with cereal to maximum capacity to the nearest 100 cm³.
    What should the setting be?

6   A box contains 40 oranges whose weights are shown in the following frequency
    table:

Weight (g)	70	80	90	100	110	120	Total
Frequency	2	6	10	11	7	4	40
weight × frequency	140	480					

Use this information to calculate the following to an appropriate level of accuracy:

a) mean weight of the apples

b) median weight of the apples

c) modal weight of the apples

d) the range in the weights of apples

7 A factory has 400 employees who are paid by the hour at the following rates:

Hourly wage in pence	£3 < £4	£4 < £5	£5 < £6	£6 < £7	£7 < £8	£8 < £9
No. of workers	10	25	134	85	69	77

a) Calculate the the following:

   i)   mean hourly wage (hint: use mid value)

   ii) median hourly wage

   iii) modal hourly wage

b) All the values found in part a) are measures of average. Which of these measures do you consider to give the best estimate of the average wage? Give your reasons.

8 Amanda wants to check she is getting good mileage from the fuel she uses in her car. She uses the following table to record her calculations.

	miles at start	miles at end	total miles	no. of litres of petrol	cost per litre	miles per litre	cost per mile
Journey 1	53478		246	30	86.4p		10.54p
Journey 2	53724	54276	552	60	88.2p	9.2	

a) For journey 1, find the mileage at the end of the journey.

b) For journey 1, find the rate in miles per litre.

c) For journey 2, calculate the cost per mile.

9 'Cut-Price' sells glass cut to any size. The recommended safety thickness and the cost depend on the area of glass sold. This information is given in the table below.

Area of glass (m^2)	Safety thickness (mm)	Cost per m^2
up to $1m^2$	3	£8.50
$1m^2$ up to $2.5\ m^2$	4	£17.50
$2.5\ m^2$ up to $9\ m^2$	6	£27.50
$9\ m^2$ up to $22\ m^2$	12	£97.00

a) A customer has a scale drawing of a house to a scale of 1:50. The measurements on the scale drawing for a pane of glass in one window are 46 mm by 34 mm. What is the recommended safety thickness for the pane of glass for this window?

b) Another customer wants to make a rough estimate of the total cost of 4 panes of glass each measuring 2.65 m by 0.55 m. He plans to round all the measurements involved in the calculation to the nearest whole number and use them to work out the approximate cost. Use his method to estimate the approximate cost.

c) Calculate the actual cost of the 4 panes of glass in part b). How close was the estimated cost to the real cost?

d) Show how the customer could have improved his method to find a better estimate of the cost.

10 The figures in the following table relate to the amount of bottled water consumed in four different countries in 1998.

Table A: Bottled Water Consumption in 1998

Country	France	Germany	US	UK
Population size	57,289,000	80,293,000	255,414,000	58,144,000
Total amount in £s paid for bottled water by population (1998)	1.374936×10^9	1.686153×10^9	2.043312×10^9	4.6512×10^8
Average consumption per head (volume in litres)	114	72	17	13

a) Using the figures in Table A, calculate the amount of bottled water consumed in total for each of the four countries. Show your method clearly.

b) Calculate the price per litre for bottled water in each country. Show your method clearly and work to an appropriate level of accuracy.

c) In which of the four countries is bottled water the most expensive? Where is it cheapest?

d) Use your calculated figures from part b) and the average consumption per head to calculate the average amount spent per person on bottled water in 1998.

Figures for the value of the average amount each person consumed in 1994 are shown in Table B. The values allow for inflation between 1994 and 1998.

Table B: Bottled Water Consumption in 1994

Country	France	Germany	US	UK
Average amount paid in £s per person for bottled water. (1994)	£22.86	£22.36	£6.78	£6.72

e) Using the answers to part d), work out the percentage change in amount paid per person for bottled water in each country from 1994 to 1998.

f) Comment on two observations you can make from your calculations.

g) Tap water costs 6.2×10^{-2} pence per litre in the UK. Roughly how many times more expensive is bottled water than tap water?

(Sources: Euromonitor, Financial Mail January 9 2000, The Hutchinson Factfinder)

11 Vijay opens a savings account and makes a deposit, which he will withdraw at the end of a year. Two banks have offered him different rates of interest on their savings accounts, as shown below.

Sure Savers Bank	**Technology Bank**
Annual Percentage Rate (APR)	Monthly rate (M)
= 10% per year	= 0.9% per month
(interest calculated at the end of the year)	(interest calculated at the end of each month and added to savings)

a) Taking M = 0.9, use the formula APR = $100 ((1 + 0.01M)^{12} - 1)$ to convert the monthly rate of interest at Technology Bank to an Annual Percentage Rate (APR).

b) Vijay plans to deposit £3000. Which bank should he use and how much more will his savings be worth at the end of a year, compared with using the other bank?

12 Harry owns 250 acres of farmland in Sussex. The government is planning to build large numbers of new houses and he can gain planning permission to build houses on 56 acres of his land. When he bought his land in the 1960s it was worth £200,000. In the year 2000, agricultural land is valued at £2500 per acre.

Using 0.4047 acres = 1 hectare and 100 hectares = 1 km^2

a) What is the area of the 250 acres in square kilometres?

b) How much is Harry's land worth for agricultural purposes in the year 2000?

c) What is the percentage increase in the value of Harry's land from the 1960s to 2000?

In January 2000, Harry obtains planning permission to build houses on 56 acres of his land. The value of land increases from £2500 per acre to £750000 per acre when planning permission to build houses is granted.

d) Compare the value of the land for agricultural use with the value of the land for houses.

e) Use a ratio to describe the change in value of Harry's 250 acres when it is used solely as agricultural land and the value of 250 acres when 56 acres can be used for building houses.

f) Show a calculation to check your result for e).

13 A college wants to improve access by building a ramp to the front entrance. It is recommended that the ramp has a ratio of 1:20 for vertical height : horizontal ground level distance.

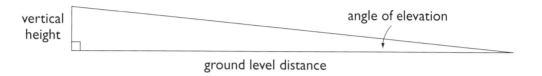

vertical height

angle of elevation

ground level distance

a) What is the angle of elevation of a ramp built to these recommendations? Give your answer to an appropriate level of accuracy.

b) The main door is above ground level. This means the vertical height of the ramp must be 0.007 metres. Find the length of the sloping surface to an appropriate level of accuracy. Show your method of calculation clearly.

c) Show how you checked your calculation.

14 'Country Kitchens' have shops in five towns of a similar size in the Midlands. They ran an advertising campaign to improve sales in all five towns for one week. The values of sales for the following week are given in the table below.

Shop	A	B	C	D	E
Amount spent on advertising	£110	£220	£320	£450	£630
Value of sales	£3100	£3600	£4700	£5400	£6100

a) Using the values given in the table above, plot a scatter graph.

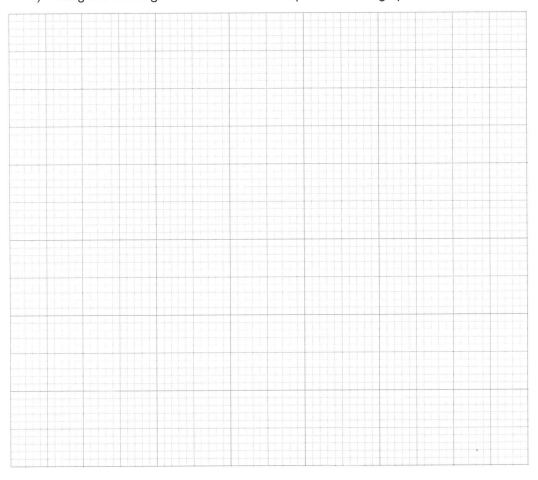

b) Draw a line of best fit through the five points.

c) Explain what your graph shows.

d) Use your graph to predict the value of the sales when spending on advertising is £500.

Exemplar Test

Key Skills external assessments are no different from any other exam or time-constrained assessment. **You must do what you are asked in the time allowed.** Straightforward as this may sound, every year many students do not do this and are then surprised when they don't get the result they hoped for!

This is an example of an Application of Number Level 3 end test. Now find a quiet place where you will not be disturbed for an hour and a half and answer the Exemplar Test. When you have finished, check your answers against those in Appendix C (pages 75-76).

EXEMPLAR TEST

LEVEL

Key Skills – Level 3

PAPER

Application of Number

WHAT YOU NEED:
- this task booklet;
- an answer booklet;
- pens with black or blue ink;
- pencils, a ruler and an eraser;
- 5 mm squared paper

ADDITIONAL AIDS:
- a scientific calculator;
- bilingual dictionaries may be used.

THERE ARE TWO PARTS TO THIS PAPER:
Part 1 – Short answer questions (25 marks)

Part 2 – Extended answer question (25 marks)

TIME ALLOWED – 1 HOUR 30 MINUTES.

To complete this activity successfully you will need to:

- complete both parts of the paper;
- write clearly so that your work can be easily understood;
- show all your working out.

Instructions to candidates

- Write your personal details in the spaces provided in your answer booklet.
- Do not open this task booklet until you are told to do so by the supervisor.
- Read each question carefully and attempt all questions.
- Write in black or blue ink only.
- Make sure you write legibly in the spaces provided.
- Make sure your meaning is clear.
- If you use extra paper, make sure that it has your name and candidate number on it and is attached securely to the task booklet.
- At the end of the assessment hand your task booklet, your answer booklet and all notes to the supervisor.

PART 1 SHORT ANSWER QUESTIONS

1 Jess has to quickly work out an estimate of $\dfrac{784}{39.2 \times 0.47}$ in her head.

Show a method which she could use.

Use it to give an estimate for the value of the calculation. *(2 marks)*

2 This scale drawing shows the front view of a garage.

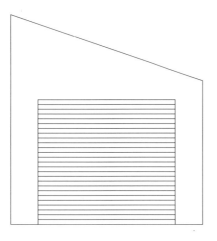

Scale 1 : 80

a) What is the actual length of the sloping edge of the garage roof? *(1 mark)*

b) Work out the actual area of the garage door. *(1 mark)*

c) The garage roof is a rectangle 6 m long.

Draw a scale diagram of the garage roof, to a scale of 1:80. *(1 mark)*

3 A store cafeteria is providing packed lunches for 54 employees. This will include 2 filled rolls each. The requests are for 50 ham, 20 cheese and 38 tuna rolls.

All the rolls will be spread with butter and include lettuce and tomato as well as the requested filling.

The table below shows how many rolls a given ingredient will fill.

INGREDIENTS	NO. OF FILLED ROLLS	AMOUNT OF INGREDIENT NEEDED FOR ROLLS REQUESTED
1 kg butter	200	
1 kg tomatoes	25	
1 kg ham	20	
1 kg cheese	30	
1 tin tuna	10	
1 lettuce	15	

Copy the table and complete the end column to show the ingredients needed to meet the requests. Give your results to appropriate levels of accuracy. *(3 marks)*

4   The population of Kenya has been increasing by 4.5% per year.

   a) After how many years could you expect its population to have doubled?   (*2 marks*)

   b) Give two factors which could affect your forecast in part a).   (*1 mark*)

5   The bar chart below shows the number of children per family in 50 families.

Number of children in a sample of families

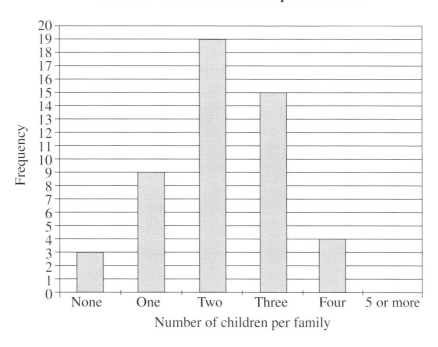

Number of children per family

   a) What is the mean number of children per family?   (*2 marks*)

   b) Another sample of 50 families has a mean number of children of 2.36 children per family and a mode of one child per family.

   What does this tell you about the number of families with 3 or more children in this second sample, compared with the number in the first sample?

   Give a reason to support your answer.   (*2 marks*)

6   A community charity is allowed to reclaim VAT on some of the items it buys.

   The charity buys 15 tables at £63.00 each, including VAT at $17\frac{1}{2}\%$.

   How much VAT might the charity reclaim altogether?   (*2 marks*)

7   A swimming pool is 21.0 metres long by 15.6 metres wide. It has a level bottom (floor). The initial quantity of water in the pool is 90 000 gallons.

   [1 gallon is approximately 4.55 litres, 1000 litres = 1 m^3.]

   a) The amount of chlorine required to maintain the quantity of water in the pool is 80 parts per million (80 ppm).

   How many litres of chlorine are required for the pool?   (*1 mark*)

   b) How many more gallons of water and chlorine mixture are required to provide a depth of 1.5 metres in the pool?   (*2 marks*)

8   A store has a cafeteria that bakes its own cakes. The recipe for a fruitcake mixture is:

INGREDIENTS	PARTS BY WEIGHT
butter	3
sugar	3
flour	3
dried fruit	4
powdered egg	4
milk	2.75
salt	trace
baking powder	0.25

a) Find the actual weight in grams of flour and baking powder used for 3 kg of the cake mixture. *(2 marks)*

b) The baking time for a cake depends on its weight and this is shown in a graph.

Baking time for fruitcake

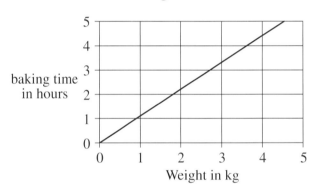

Estimate the baking time for the 3 kg cake. *(1 mark)*

c) The original recipe gave the baking temperature as 350°F. Modern ovens use °C and the conversion formula is

$F = \frac{9}{5}C + 32$, where F is temperature in °F and C is temperature in °C

Calculate the equivalent temperature in °C to appropriate accuracy. *(2 marks)*

PART 2 EXTENDED ANSWER QUESTION

9   Fitness Training

People are becoming aware of possible connections between "Body Mass Index" and fitness. A person's Body Mass Index (BMI) gives a rough measure of how under- or over-weight the person might be.

Eleven people volunteered to take part in an experiment to measure their relative fitness and then compare the results with their BMI. The people were in two groups, group A and group B.

In the fitness test, each person relaxed for 10 minutes (to establish their resting pulse rate P_R) and then undertook a specified number of step-ups over a four minute period. The person's pulse rate was measured immediately after finishing the step-ups (P_O), and again after 6 minutes of rest (P_6).

A person's fitness can be estimated by how quickly their heart rate recovers after a period of strenuous exercise. A measure of fitness, H, can be calculated using the formula

$$H = \frac{P_O - P_6}{P_O - P_R}$$

The results are given in Table 1.

Table 1							
	PERSON	P_R beats/min	P_O beats/min	P_6 beats/min	Height (m)	Weight (kg)	H
Group A	G	86	144	88	1.62	46	0.97
	H	90	134	97	1.57	64	0.84
	J	76	129	77	1.74	78	0.98
	K	82	146	83	1.79	73	0.98
	L	75	135	79	1.76	82	0.93
Group B	M	72	100	76	1.58	48	
	N	78	95	78	1.64	54	
	P	68	120	80	1.78	54	
	Q	72	116	72	1.74	58	
	R	80	112	80	1.80	72	
	S	68	120	78	1.54	64	

Table 2

Body Mass Index

ht(m)	1.50	1.52	1.54	1.56	1.58	1.60	1.62	1.64	1.66	1.68	1.70	1.72	1.74	1.76	1.78	1.80
wt(kg)																
40	18	17	17	16	16	16	15	15	15	14	14	14	13	13	13	12
42	19	18	18	17	17	16	16	16	15	15	15	14	14	14	13	13
44	20	19	19	18	18	17	17	16	16	16	15	15	15	14	14	14
46	20	20	19	19	18	18	18	17	17	16	16	16	15	15	15	14
48	21	21	20	20	19	19	18	18	17	17	17	16	16	15	15	15
50	22	22	21	21	20	20	19	19	18	18	17	17	17	16	16	15
52	23	23	22	21	21	20	20	19	19	18	18	18	17	17	16	16
54	24	23	23	22	22	21	21	20	20	19	19	18	18	17	17	17
56	25	24	24	23	22	22	21	21	20	20	19	19	18	18	18	17
58	26	25	24	24	23	23	22	22	21	21	20	20	19	19	18	18
60	27	26	25	25	24	23	23	22	22	21	21	20	20	19	19	19
62	28	27	26	25	25	24	24	23	22	22	21	21	20	20	20	19
64	28	28	27	26	26	25	24	24	23	23	22	22	21	21	20	20
66	29	29	28	27	26	26	25	25	24	23	23	22	22	21	21	20
68	30	29	29	28	27	27	26	25	25	24	24	23	22	22	21	21
70	31	30	30	29	28	27	27	26	25	25	24	24	23	23	22	22
72	32	31	30	30	29	28	27	27	26	26	25	24	24	23	23	22
74	33	32	31	30	30	29	28	28	27	26	26	25	24	24	23	23
76	34	33	32	31	30	30	29	28	28	27	26	26	25	25	24	23
78	35	34	33	32	31	30	30	29	28	28	27	26	26	25	25	24
80	36	35	34	33	32	31	30	30	29	28	28	27	26	26	25	25
82	36	35	35	34	33	32	31	30	30	29	28	28	27	26	26	25
84	37	36	35	35	34	33	32	31	30	30	29	28	28	27	27	26
86	38	37	36	35	34	34	33	32	31	30	30	29	28	28	27	27
88	39	38	37	36	35	34	34	33	32	31	30	30	29	28	28	27
90	40	39	38	37	36	35	34	33	33	32	31	30	30	29	28	28

a) Use the information in Table 1 to calculate the values for *H* for the members of group B (the values of *H* for group A have already been calculated).

   Make it clear how you calculated at least one of the values of *H*. *(4 marks)*

b) Find the range of *H* values for each group.

   Choose, then find an appropriate average (mean, median or mode) for each of the two sets of values of *H* and give a reason for your choice.

   Show clearly one of your calculations of average. *(5 marks)*

c) Use your results from part a) and part b) to compare the levels of fitness of the two groups.

   Give at least two reasons to support your conclusions. *(2 marks)*

d) Using Table 2, find the Body Mass Index for each of the eleven volunteers.
   Present the values for *H* and BMI in a suitable table. *(4 marks)*

e) Present a suitable, clearly labelled graph showing *H* plotted against BMI for the eleven volunteers (plot BMI across the page and *H* upwards). *(7 marks)*

f) Describe any ways in which BMI and *H* appear to be related. Comment on the possibility of estimating an individual's *H* value from their Body Mass Index. *(3 marks)*

Producing your portfolio of evidence

Getting started

The object of building a portfolio is to demonstrate in a relevant context and for a real purpose that you can:

- apply your number skills and show you can tackle numerical problems
- collect, record, interpret and present data

The contents of a Level 3 portfolio

- What work will go in it?
- Think about your studies. What do they involve? Do you need number skills?
- Will there be opportunities for you to use work from your studies for your Application of Number portfolio?
- Do the subjects you study involve collecting information or data?

If you can, discuss this with your teachers.

Sometimes evidence may not seem obvious if you are studying mainly humanities/arts subjects. See Chapter 9 (pages 63-64) for suggestions on what to do if this is the case.

Identify opportunities to generate evidence for your portfolio

- Make a list of the subjects you study.
- Make a list for your portfolio of any opportunities your subjects give to do work on data collection.

Most subjects you are studying will offer opportunities for you to develop examples of your number skills. Don't forget all of these qualifications have Key Skills sign-posted within their specifications. Ask your tutor or college librarian to help you get a copy. You can then identify where you could cover number as part of your main programme of study. Don't forget Enrichment Studies and any employment you have can also provide valuable Key Skills evidence.

To help identify opportunities for demonstrating your number skills, fill in Table 1.

Table 1: Identifying opportunities for generating evidence

Subjects you study/Enrichment programmes/Employment	Assignments/Topics involving data collection and calculations

What evidence will go in my portfolio?

If the subjects you study lend themselves to generating evidence for your Application of Number portfolio, then use these assignments. You will need to decide how to use this work as evidence for your portfolio. Table 2 outlines in a simple way the contents of an Application of Number portfolio. The evidence requirements are explained in more detail in this and later chapters. As your understanding of what work you need to do grows, you may need to return to Table 2 and review your plans. Using the information from Table 1, try to fill in Table 2 as far as you can with the assignment work you could use in your portfolio. A blank version of Table 2 can be found in Appendix D for you to complete.

If you can, check with your subject teachers what the work involves. The assignment brief may give guidance on what evidence to include for Key Skills. It is important to establish first what evidence will occur naturally in your programme of study. Do this work first; then think about whether you need to find evidence for a second activity. It is unlikely you will cover all the requirements for the portfolio in one activity.

If the subjects you study do not offer any opportunities for generating evidence for Application of Number, you will need to design a piece of work for yourself. See Chapter 9 for advice on how to do this.

Table 2: Contents of a Level 3 Application of Number Portfolio

Application of Number portfolio requirements for Level 3	Evidence
N3.1 Plan and interpret information from **TWO** different sources, including a large data set (50+ items).	Source one
	Source two
	Large data set
N3.2 Carry out multi-stage calculations to do with: a) amounts and sizes b) scales and proportions c) handling statistics d) rearranging and using formulae You should work with a large data set on at least **ONE** occasion.	A
	B
	C
	D
	Calculations with large set of data
N3.3 Interpret results of your calculations, present your findings and justify your methods. You must use at least one **GRAPH**, one **CHART** and one **DIAGRAM**.	Graph
	Chart
	Diagram

Defining the terms

A number of terms, such as complex, multi-stage, etc. are used in the Unit Specification. These are explained below.

COMPLEX – Complex subjects and materials present a number of ideas, some of which may be abstract. For Application of Number, a complex activity is one requiring students to consider carefully the nature and sequence of tasks they undertake when planning how to obtain and use information to meet their purpose.

A **SUBSTANTIAL ACTIVITY** is one that includes a number of related tasks, where the results of one task will affect the carrying out of others. In Application of Number, a substantial activity will involve obtaining and interpreting information, using this information when carrying out calculations and explaining how the results of your calculations meet the purpose of the activity.

MULTI-STAGE – Calculations that involve at least two interrelated stages, i.e. where the results from one stage are used to provide some of the data for calculations at the next stage.

Understanding the Unit Specification for Part B

First, look at Part B of the Unit Specification for Level 3 Application of Number in Appendix A (page 68).

> **Part B Application of Number Level 3**
>
> **Plan and carry through at least one substantial and complex activity that includes tasks for N3.1, N3.2 and N3.3**

> **What does it actually mean?**
>
> **Choose one piece of work where you have to collect a large set of data – at least 50 items. Try to cover as much of the criteria for Level 3 Application of Number as you can in this piece of work. This is where careful planning is crucial. If necessary, you can complete the evidence requirements with a second piece of work.**

Table 3 is designed to help you understand the specifications more clearly and to explain, as simply as possible, what evidence you need to include in your portfolio.

- In the left-hand column of the table is what the specifications require.

- The right-hand column gives guidance and suggestions on how to produce this evidence.

Table 3: What evidence do you need?

What the specifications say:	What you need to do:
N3.1 Plan and interpret information from **TWO** different sources, including a large data set (50+ items).	Plan an activity that involves collecting a large set of data (50+ items). This should provide you with the opportunity of gathering information from two different sources. If it is only possible to find information from one source, then another activity will have to be planned to meet the specification. Try to avoid this if possible. The second source of information could be a graph on the topic under investigation.

Evidence must show you can:	
1. Plan how to obtain and use information required to meet the purpose of your activity.	Your work must include evidence of planning. This could be an action plan or a detailed description of the approach you took. You must also state your aim and why you are doing it; ideally this will link in with the requirements of coursework from other subjects. You must include a description of the activity, what information you need to find and how you will go about finding it. • State the purpose of your activity – explain what you are trying to find out. • Include evidence to show that you planned how to approach the problem. • Write a description of what you did.
2. Obtain the relevant information.	The data you found should be listed clearly, perhaps in a table. Give details of the source of your information.
3. Choose appropriate methods for obtaining the results you need and justify your choice.	In the description of your approach to collecting the information, you must explain how you intend to use the information, e.g. what calculations and graphs you will include.

What the specifications say:	What you need to do:
N3.2 Carry out multi-stage calculations to do with: a) amounts and sizes b) scales and proportions c) handling statistics d) rearranging and using formulae You should work with a large data set on at least **ONE** occasion.	It may not be possible to find one natural activity that can provide opportunities for all four types of calculation. So, cover as many types as you can in your first activity and then do the remaining ones in your second activity. Remember: each activity you do must meet all assessment criteria for N3.1, 3.2 and 3.3. If your first activity involved 50+ items, the second activity can be done with a smaller sample. At this level, calculations must involve at least two steps, i.e. where results from one stage are used to provide some data for calculations at the next stage.

Evidence must show you can:	
1. Carry out calculations to appropriate levels of accuracy, clearly showing your methods.	Make sure you show all your working and the stages within it in detail, even if you have used a spreadsheet. For example, if you use a formula such as 'Mean = $\Sigma x/n$', write down the formula and then do your calculations. In this way you will have included some evidence of N3.2d as well as N3.2c. You will also need to show evidence of rearranging formulae.

2. Check methods and results to help ensure errors are found and corrected.

This is a difficult one! First make sure any calculations are correct. Ask someone else to check them. Make a note in your work of any checks you make. You will have to decide what checking is appropriate. You could estimate and make a rough calculation. You could check your answers by inverse calculations or by annotating work to show evidence of checking.

Another approach is to check your results give answers that make sense and are about the size you would expect. For example, if you have a large data set, you can judge whether calculated values for means and standard deviation make sense by looking at the shape and spread of the distribution.

Some evidence of checking must be included otherwise you will not have met all the criteria.

What the specifications say:

N3.3 Interpret results of your calculations, present your findings and justify your methods. You must use at least one **GRAPH**, one **CHART** and one **DIAGRAM**.

You may use any suitable type of graph, chart or diagram. The following list gives you some examples.

graphs: e.g. line graphs, histograms, scatter graphs, frequency polygons, cumulative frequency graphs

charts: e.g. bar charts, pie charts, flow charts

diagrams: e.g. frequency tables, scale drawings, network diagrams, box and whisker plots, scientific diagrams, maps, plans

Evidence must show you can:

1. Select appropriate methods of presentation and justify your choice.

With the purpose of your work always in mind, present your data using a suitable type of graph. You can draw this by hand or use a computer. Whatever you do, you must ensure the graph is drawn accurately and the scales are correct and make sense. Remember to give your graph a heading such as 'Bar chart to show…'.

You must justify your use of this technique. For example, explain why a bar chart was the most appropriate method to use to present your data.

2. Present your findings effectively.

You must make sure that whatever methods you use are effective in showing the main features of the data. For example, if your data shows a trend over a period of time, the most effective graph to use would be a line graph. If you needed to show the relationship between two factors, a scatter graph may be best. As well as drawing the graph, describe in words what it shows. Link your interpretation to your original purpose.

3. Explain how the results of your calculations relate to the purpose of your activity.

Look at the results of your calculations. Describe what they show. How do they fulfil the purpose of your activity? Do they give further support to what your graphs show? Make sure a written explanation of this is included in your evidence.

Sample portfolio for Application of Number Level 3

Now you have some idea of what you need to do, look at the following example of a Level 3 portfolio, created for this book. It is made up of only two pieces of work. The first and main piece, **'Investigation to show if there is a difference between the length of words in tabloid and broadsheet newspapers'**, is an example of a **substantial** and **complex** data collection activity of over 50 items. It covers most of the evidence for the Application of Number portfolio. The second piece, **'The Walk'**, also involved collecting data, but used a small sample only. All aspects of the criteria for N3.1, 3.2 and 3.3 are covered.

Look at this work closely to see how the criteria in the Unit Specifications are met. This is explained in detail in Chapter 8.

TIP

Each of the pages in the portfolio has been numbered using Roman numerals (i-xi). You are advised to number the pages in your portfolio to help you to make reference to all the relevant evidence.

NOTE

This portfolio is intended as guidance **only**. Any work you produce must be original and unaided to meet the Unit Specification.

INVESTIGATION TO SHOW IF THERE IS A DIFFERENCE BETWEEN THE LENGTH OF WORDS IN TABLOID AND BROADSHEET NEWSPAPERS

i

Aims

As part of my English Language studies, I am going to compare the number of letters in a word in broadsheet and tabloid newspapers. I have chosen to look at the following newspapers for my investigation:
The Sun, Daily Mail, The Times and The Guardian.

My hypothesis is that broadsheet newspapers have a more sophisticated readership and therefore the vocabulary they use will be more complex.

Once I have collected my data, I will use lots of different/relevant techniques to analyse my data to help me draw conclusions and see if my prediction about the papers is actually true.

By using articles about the same subjects for the same day, I hope to achieve some consistency. I am using papers from Friday 1st October, and the article will be about the nuclear disaster in Japan.

This investigation is worthwhile as I will be able to see if the length of words in tabloids and broadsheets differ. The findings will be a representation of the whole paper for every day, and will indicate whether or not you need to be a more advanced reader and have a larger vocabulary to understand the broadsheet newspapers.

The population is the words and I am counting the number of letters in each word.

When I have obtained this data, I will be using it to support my English language coursework looking at the topic of literacy levels within the population of Britain.

Sampling Method

I have chosen the same article from each paper. I chose that particular article because it was the only article that all four papers had in common. I decided that I would take words from the beginning, middle and end of the article, so that I would get an overall picture of the article. First of all I found the beginning, middle and end paragraphs of the articles. In the tabloid newspapers I sometimes had to use two paragraphs instead of one – if I did not have enough words in the paragraph I was using then I went on to use the next one as well. I took a sample of the number of letters in a word in a particular article in the papers and I used this to represent the whole population of words in each newspaper on different days.

I counted all of the words in the paragraphs, writing down the numbers as I went along. I then used systematic sampling by taking every fourth word to get my data sample.

Raw Data

Number of letters per word

The Sun

Beg: ①10, 3, 7,⑤8, 3, 6,③2, 7, 2,⑤4, 5, 8,②6, 4, 7,②4, 7, 5,①7, 2, 1,⑦2, 9, 10,⑦5, 4, 4,⑤

Middle: 3, 4, 8,④5, 7, 4,⑥7, 4, 6,④2, 4, 4,③1, 7, 5,⑤9, 2, 8,⑤7, 3, 3,③6, 2, 2,⑦6, 5, 5,③6, 3, 9,③

End: 2, 10, 9,⑦6, 2, 1,④4, 3, 3,③8, 6, 3,④2, 4, 2,⑧2, 3, 6,⑨4, 10, 4,⑦3, 6, 5,④1, 5, 4,②7, 7, 8,④6, 7, 2

The Daily Mail

Beg: ④4, 6, 6,③5, 2, 3,⑥7, 4, 7,②4, 7, 2,⑬6, 6, 2,⑤5, 6, 7,④4, 3, 4,⑤3, 6, 6,③2, 7, 2,②1, 5, 4

Middle: ⑦8, 1, 6,④5, 3, 9,⑥4, 1, 4,②3, 5, 4,③3, 6, 2,⑬7, 2, 2,③5, 7, 8,④2, 5, 5,⑦2, 11, 4,⑥8

End: ②10, 9, 7,⑨4, 7, 5,③8, 3, 7,④3, 6, 6,④2, 8, 2,⑧3, 4, 4,②7, 2, 4,②5, 4, 2,⑤2, 2, 1,④4, 3, 3

The Times

Beg: ②8, 2, 1,⑧7, 10, 5,⑥9, 6, 7,②5, 3, 6,⑨5, 3, 3,⑤2, 4, 9,②6, 2, 3,⑦9, 5, 4,⑤6, 1, 5,⑦2

Middle: 10, 8,⑪10, 2, 5,⑥8, 3, 6,⑥1, 7, 6,④7, 2, 6,⑦10, 7, 5,⑩8, 9, 3,⑧7, 5, 5,⑤7, 7, 5,②2, 11, 3,⑥2, 1, 7

End: ⑩, 9, 7, 8,②7, 8, 4,③2, 6, 3,⑨6, 2, 4,⑧2, 8, 3,④4, 2, 7,②4, 3, 2,④3, 2, 2,⑬3, 6, 2,⑧

The Guardian

Beg: ③, 6, 5, 7,⑧5, 9, 3,⑥12, 5, 5,⑦9, 4, 5,②1, 8, 7,④5, 10, 6,⑪6, 1, 7,⑥2, 3, 8,④3, 5, 3,⑨9

Middle: 4, 4,⑥3, 6, 3,⑤3, 8, 6,⑨8, 6, 3,⑥4, 7, 9,④2, 5, 7,⑤6, 3, 8,⑧3, 2, 2,⑨12, 6, 1,⑩6, 7, 9,④3, 8, 8,

End: ②, 3, 3, 8,⑥2, 3, 12,⑩5, 2, 7,⑨7, 5, 2,⑥9, 2, 4,⑤7, 10, 8, ⑩6, 2, 8,⑬4, 8, 5,⑦2, 6, 4,②7, 6

DATA IN A TABLE

No. of Letters	The Sun	The Daily Mail	The Times	The Guardian
1	2	0	0	0
2	3	6	5	3
3	6	5	2	1
4	6	7	3	4
5	5	3	3	3
6	1	3	4	6
7	5	2	3	2
8	1	1	4	2
9	1	1	2	4
10	0	0	2	3
11	0	0	1	1
12	0	0	0	0
13	0	2	1	1

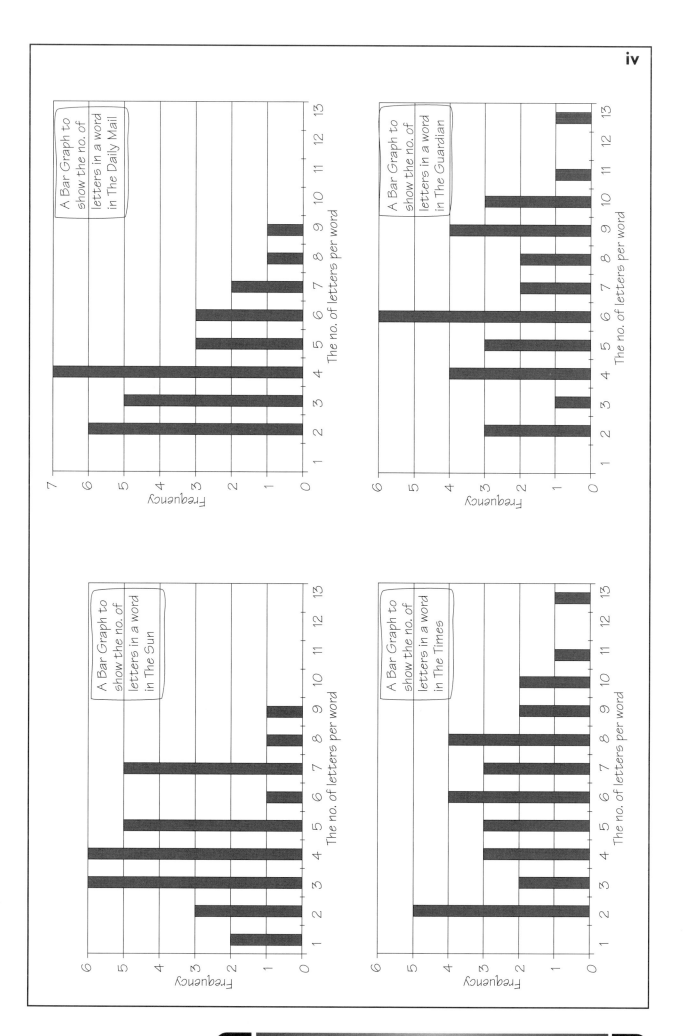

BAR GRAPH INTERPRETATION

I have drawn bar graphs, because they show clearly the spread/shape of the data. I could have represented the data in a stem and leaf diagram, which would have shown exactly the same thing, but I thought bar graphs would show it more clearly. The bar graphs also allow me to compare my data with my hypothesis and see if I was right or wrong. I haven't drawn a histogram because then I would have to group my data and if I did that my data would not be as clear and as easy to compare and interpret.

The Sun has the smallest spread of data, with a peak at three and four and a smaller peak at seven, but most of the data is clumped around the first peak. When the data has two peaks like this it is known as a bi-modal distribution. From just looking at the graph you can see that The Sun newspaper has shorter words than the other papers generally, so I think that my initial hypothesis was right.

The Daily Mail has a larger range of data, but most of the data is clumped around the beginning, implying that more of the words have fewer letters in them. This means the data has a positive skew. From just looking at the graph I would say that The Daily Mail has the second shortest words, which makes my initial hypothesis correct.

The Times has data that seems to be very evenly spread with a slight positive skew, but at the same time the data is almost symmetrical. The Times generally has longer words than the first two papers from interpreting the graphs, which again backs up my hypothesis.

The Guardian, on the other hand, has a very obvious peak right in the centre, which is almost a symmetrical distribution. From looking at the graphs I think that The Guardian has the longest words, but only slightly longer than the words in The Times. I did not predict this, as I thought that The Times and The Guardian would have very similar length words.

Checking/Means

Looking at my bar charts I would estimate the means to be:

The Sun, mean estimated to be 4

The Times, mean estimated to be 6

The Daily Mail, mean estimated to be 4

The Guardian, mean estimated to be 6

Checking/Standard Deviations

Looking at my bar charts for The Sun and Daily Mail, there appears to be less variation in the length of words in The Sun than in The Daily Mail.

Comparing The Times and The Guardian, The Times seems to have a more consistent pattern and there appears to be a wider variation in The Guardian, so I would expect The Guardian to have a larger standard deviation than The Times.

I think it would be a good idea to look at an average result, so I can compare the length of words more easily and see which papers have the longest and which have the shortest words on average. I think that the best average to find would be the mean. The median and mode are not as good for my data. I have not done the median as it would be better done on a cumulative frequency graph and, as my data is discrete, this method is not very appropriate. I have not done the mode as it only tells you the most frequently occurring number of letters in a word, but this may only have one extra letter in it or the data may be strangely skewed. For example, if I took the mode for The Times it would be two, but on the whole the data has much higher values than that of The Sun, which happens to have a higher mode.

I will use the mean to check if my prediction was entirely accurate and to tell me if my bar chart interpretations were correct.

Mean = $\bar{X}$ = $\Sigma fx/n$

The Sun = 133/30 = 4.43 (2dp)

The Daily Mail = 145/30 = 4.83 (2dp)

The Times = 182/30 = 6.07 (2dp)

The Guardian = 196/30 = 6.53 (2dp)

From finding out the mean, I can clearly see that The Sun has shorter words compared to all of the other papers and The Guardian has the longest words on average. The means back up what I found from my bar charts and The Guardian does have slightly longer words on the whole. The mean also proves my prediction to be right apart from the fact that The Guardian has slightly longer words. On average the words are almost 0.5 letters longer. The difference between the longest and shortest word (on average) is not huge, but is significant enough to make the papers with a higher mean slightly more complex. The difference is 2.10.

Checking

My calculated values for means appear to make sense in terms of my original data.

If I now work out the combined mean of tabloid and broadsheet papers, it will allow me to compare on a more general basis, rather than just looking at the individual papers.

The Combined Mean

$\bar{X}$ = $\Sigma x/n_1$ $\bar{Y}$ = $\Sigma y/n_2$

Rearranging equations: $\Sigma x = n_1\bar{X}$ $\Sigma y = n_2\bar{Y}$

$\Sigma x = 30 \times 4.43 = 133$

$\Sigma y = 30 \times 4.83 = 145$

Combined Mean = $(\Sigma x + \Sigma y)/(n_1 + n_2)$

Combined Mean for Tabloids = (133+145)/60 = 4.63 (2dp)

Combined Mean for Broadsheets = (182+196)/60 = 6.30 (2dp)

This shows clearly that an average broadsheet newspaper will have more letters per word than a tabloid, which is exactly what I predicted. The difference is 1.67, which is not all that significant.

I did think about drawing box and whisker plots to show the range of my data pictorially, but working out the median and interquartile range is not very appropriate for my data, as it is discrete. So I think the standard deviation would be more appropriate for working out the spread of the data.

I am now going to work out the standard deviation of the data:

Standard Deviation

Variance = $s^2 = \Sigma x^2/n - \overline{X}^2$

Standard Deviation = s

The Sun, variance = $715/30 - 4.43^2 = 4.1616$

Standard deviation = 2.04 (2dp)

The Daily Mail, variance = $945/30 - 4.83^2 = 8.1225$

Standard deviation = 2.85 (2dp)

The Times, variance = $1360/30 - 6.07^2 = 8.5264$

Standard deviation = 2.92 (2dp)

The Guardian, variance = $1516/30 - 6.53^2 = 7.8512$

Standard deviation = 2.80 (2dp)

Checking

My estimated value for standard deviation is higher for The Daily Mail than The Sun. However, the standard deviation for The Guardian is less than that for The Times, which was not expected. Nevertheless, these values are close, showing a more consistent pattern between the two broadsheet papers.

The standard deviation shows the average deviation from the mean. The larger the number, the more spread out the data. Two-thirds of the data should be within one standard deviation from the mean; ninety-five percent should be within two standard deviations from the mean and ninety-nine point five percent should be within three standard deviations from the mean. I have used standard deviation instead of range, because standard deviation takes into account the frequency as well as the spread.

My standard deviations don't differ all that much, but The Sun does have the smallest standard deviation, which means that most of the numbers are closer to the low mean.

The Guardian has the second smallest standard deviation. This shows that most of the words have more letters in them and it does not vary all that much.

The Daily Mail has the second highest standard deviation, which means that the data is slightly more spread out, and shows that the paper has long as well as short words. This makes the paper a little more complex than The Sun newspaper.

The Times has the highest standard deviation showing that the data is the most spread out and, even though the mean is high, the data also has quite a few low values, causing a larger spread. This means that, on average, The Guardian has longer words than The Times.

My investigation to see if broadsheet newspapers are more complex and have longer words compared to tabloid newspapers has been conclusive. I have found out that broadsheet newspapers have longer words than tabloid newspapers. I have also found out the order in which the four papers (The Sun, The Daily Mail, The Times and The Guardian) I was using come in, in relation to the length of words they contain on average.

I have found out using my bar charts and the mean that The Sun has the shortest words on average. Also, using the standard deviation, I have found that the spread is very small, meaning that the words in The Sun are all generally short, making it the least complex paper.

I have found that The Daily Mail has the second shortest words from looking at the mean and, according to the standard deviation, the paper has a slightly larger range of length of words compared to The Sun, making it slightly more complex.

The Times has a larger average length of word compared to The Sun and The Daily Mail, but has a larger range, implying that The Times does have shorter words as well as longer words. It is more complex than the last two papers but still has quite a few short words.

The Guardian seems to be the most complex paper of them all. It has the largest mean and the smallest standard deviation, implying that most of the words are longer than in the other three papers.

From analysing my data I have found out what I predicted at the beginning, apart from the fact that I did not expect The Guardian to use longer words compared to The Times. My investigation has been worthwhile, as I have clearly found out that the length of words in broadsheet and tabloid newspapers does vary and the broadsheet newspapers use longer words than the tabloids. This is significant for the study levels of literacy within the population.

I have been able to draw conclusions about my data, which are a representation of the whole population of words in the paper on that particular day as well as on different days.

To improve my investigation and to give a better representation of the papers as a whole, as well as on different days, I would need to have a larger sample of data from the papers, comparing the papers on different days. I could also see if there is a difference in the different sections of the paper, for example whether the papers use the same complexity of language in the sport section, compared to the front page. I would also need to look at the length of sentences and paragraphs to decide whether or not the complexity of language is all that different. The quality of the investigation could be improved by finding out these extra things and possibly using different techniques to represent the data. By doing these things I would get a much more accurate conclusion. I was not able to investigate the points made above as there was a limit on the time, which restricted me to undertaking a much smaller scale investigation.

I now need to obtain statistics on literacy levels for adults and I will be using them and the information from this investigation in my English language project.

MAKING CONNECTIONS

By getting to know the Unit Specifications for all of your Key Skills you can start to make connections. Pieces of work that you use for evidence in one Key Skill may also cover some of the evidence requirements of another Key Skill.

Evidence you create for this portfolio may also cover:

C	3.1b	3.2	3.3
IT	3.1	3.2	3.3
LP	3.1		

★ See page 8 for further information on the wider Key Skills.
Visit www.qca.org.uk for detailed Unit Specifications.

"The Walk"

Aim and Plan (N3.1)

I am organising a sponsored walk as part of my Enrichment Studies programme. This is to raise money for the local conservation trust. In order for it to be successful I need to plan the walk in advance.

The most reliable way of collecting the information for this walk is to use Ordinance Survey Pathfinder Maps for the area I wish to walk. Using OS Maps 1287 and 1306, I planned a day's walk on the South Downs that could be undertaken by a reasonably fit person who enjoys outdoor activities and a challenge. Using the maps, I noted the grid reference of each of the main points on the walk. I then used the map scale to calculate the distance and roughly estimate the walking time. I need to take into account the nature of the terrain and the steepness of the path.

First I used the maps to plan the route and noted the following grid references.

Grid reference	Place name, where appropriate
08081109	Chantry Post
07081004	Lee Farm
08030805	Michelgrove
09010805	Myrtle Grove Farm
11000808	Roman Well
09051107	Southdowns Way
08181109	Chantry Post

(N3.2)

Using the map scale, 4 cm to 1 km, I measured the distances between the points on the map and calculated the distances between, as shown in this table:

Place name, where appropriate	Distances on map	Actual distance, 4cm = 1 km	Distance in miles 0.625 km = 1 mi.
Chantry Post	0 cm	0 km	0 mi.
Lee Farm	9 cm	9/4 = 2.25 km	2.25 x 0.625 = 1.41 mi. (2dp)
Michelgrove	8.4 cm	8.4/4 = 2.1 km	2.1 x 0.625 = 1.31 mi. (2dp)
Myrtle Grove Farm	3.2 cm	3.2/4 = 0.8 km	0.8 x 0.625 = 0.5 mi.
Roman Well	9.8 cm	9.8/4 = 2.45 km	2.45 x 0.625 = 1.53 mi. (2dp)
Southdowns Way	13.5 cm	13.5/4 = 3.375 km	3.375 x 0.625 = 2.11 mi. (2dp)
Chantry Post	3.2 cm	3.2/4 = 0.8 km	0.8 x 0.625 = 0.5 mi.

Using the distances noted in the table, I combined them, and found the total distance was 7.36 miles.

Walking Speed   x

I estimate the total time for this walk to be 7.36/3 = 2.45 hours, assuming the average walking pace to be about 3 mph. Roughly, this is about a $2\frac{1}{2}$ hour walk at an average steady pace, without breaks.

Checking

I have walked this path and know this is a long walk that takes about 3 hours with a stop for a rest. I would judge the calculated distance of just over 7 miles is about right, although it always feels more like at least 10 miles. The distance of 7.36 miles is a sensible answer.

Altitude and distance

I then looked at the walk in terms of altitude and height climbed between points. I referred to the grid points on the map and noted the height above sea level, using the contours on the map. I also calculated the cumulative distance from the starting point.

Place name, where appropriate	Height above sea level in metres	Distances on map
Chantry Post	189 m	0 cm
Lee Farm	86 m	9 cm
Michelgrove	70 m	8.4 cm, 17.4 cm
Myrtle Grove Farm	65 m	3.2 cm, 20.6 cm
Roman Well	110 m	9.8 cm, 30.4 cm
Southdowns Way	191 m	13.5 cm, 43.9 cm
Chantry Post	189 m	3.2 cm, 47.1 cm

Checking

I used the cumulative distance to check my calculations.

47.1 cm/4 = 11.775 km, 11.775 x 0.625 = 07.359375 mi. = 7.36mi., as previously calculated.

(N3.3)

Using these points I constructed a line graph to show the hills climbed on the walk. This is the best method to use to give an idea of the amount of up and down hill walking. It gives a cross-sectional representation of the walk. I have used graph paper as I found this was more accurate.

Interpretation

The graph shows that this circular walk involves a steady downhill walk for the first part, from 189 m at the starting point to 65 m at the lowest point, Myrtle Grove – a downhill walk dropping 124 m. So, the time for the first part is likely to be faster than the estimated time. However, from Myrtle Grove the walk involves a steady uphill climb to the Southdowns Way, at 191 m. This will be hard going and the walker may need a rest. So, the original estimated time of $2\frac{1}{2}$ hours may be perhaps an underestimate, and the walk may actually take 3 hours or perhaps a little more. Other factors, such as the weather will also affect walking speed.

Conclusion

Overall, I am confident that the data I have generated shows that the circular walk I have chosen is feasible for a sponsored walk and that the majority of participants will be able to complete it within a morning.

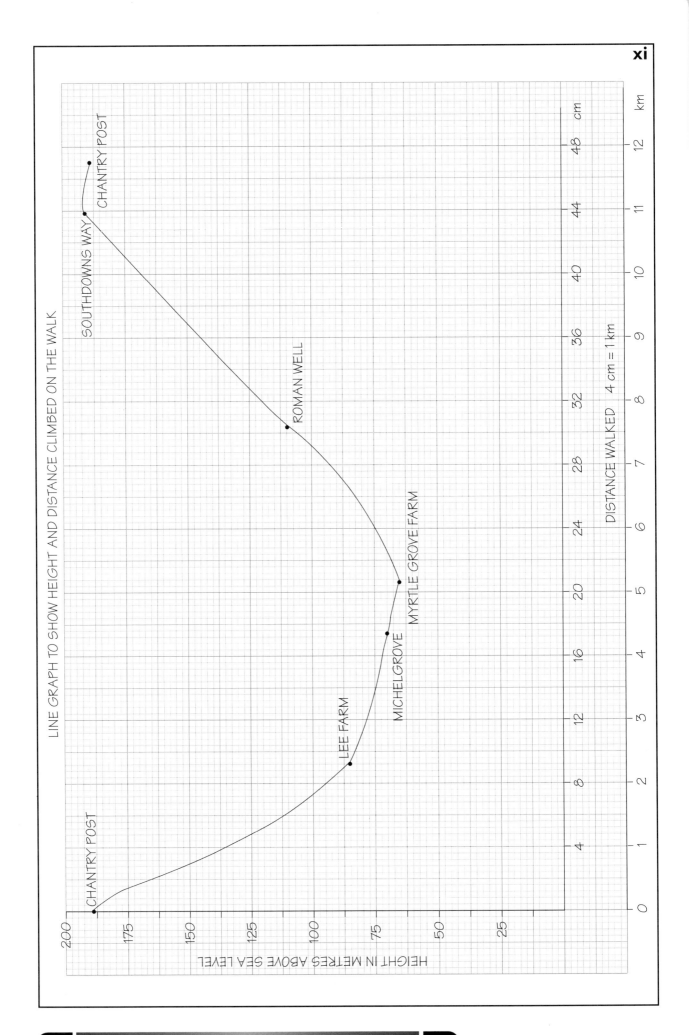

LINE GRAPH TO SHOW HEIGHT AND DISTANCE CLIMBED ON THE WALK

CHANTRY POST

SOUTHDOWNS WAY

CHANTRY POST

ROMAN WELL

LEE FARM

MICHELGROVE

MYRTLE GROVE FARM

HEIGHT IN METRES ABOVE SEA LEVEL

200
175
150
125
100
75
50
25

DISTANCE WALKED   4 cm = 1 km

km   0   1   2   3   4   5   6   7   8   9   10   11   12   km

cm   4   8   12   16   20   24   28   32   36   40   44   48   cm

xi

Sample portfolio – Activity 1

First, look at 'Investigation to show if there is a difference between the length of words in tabloid and broadsheet newspapers'.

The newspaper investigation is an example of a **substantial** and **complex** activity, involving the collection of a large data set of at least 50 items. The work covers most of the evidence elements of Level 3 Application of Number, including data collection, calculations on this data, graphical presentation and interpretation.

TIP

> **When you complete your assessment records and need to refer to the location of the evidence, give the page number from your portfolio, as done in Table 4. This will ensure you have not missed any vital evidence and will also make the task of assessment and moderation much easier.**

Table 4 shows in detail how the work covers the specifications.

Table 4: How the sample portfolio covers the specifications

What the specifications say:	Evidence covered in the newspaper investigation
N3.1 Plan and interpret information from **TWO** different sources, including a large data set (50+ items).	In this work, information has been gathered from four different newspapers: two tabloids and two broadsheets. Although evidence has been collected from four sources, they are all from the same type of source (portfolio page **i**). It involves the use of a large data set (page **ii**). *(Information from a second source will be needed.)*
Evidence must show you can:	
1. Plan how to obtain and use information required to meet the purpose of your activity.	The purpose of the activity is explained on page **i**. On page **i**, the student has given a detailed description of the method used to collect the information, and of the approach taken to gather the data and ensure it was of good quality.
2. Obtain the relevant information.	The raw data found is given on page **ii** and clearly tabulated on page **iii**.
3. Choose appropriate methods for obtaining the results you need and justify your choice.	Brief reference is made on choice of appropriate methods to prove the aim in the third paragraph on page **i**. Further justification of choices made is given as the data is analysed on pages **v** to **vii**.

What the specifications say:	Evidence covered in the newspaper investigation
N3.2 Carry out multi-stage calculations to do with: a) amounts and sizes b) scales and proportions c) handling statistics d) rearranging and using formulae You should work with a large data set on at least **ONE** occasion.	Pages **vi** to **vii** include detailed calculations for means, variance and standard deviations using a large data set. The large data set must have been used for calculations on at least one occasion. These calculations involve: a) amounts and sizes c) handling statistics d) rearranging (page **vi**) and use of formulae (pages **vi** and **vii**) *[b) has not been covered.]* The calculations are multi-stage because the student has calculated the mean and then used this value to calculate standard deviation, page **vii**, as well as combined means, page **vi**.
Evidence must show you can:	
1. Carry out calculations to appropriate levels of accuracy, clearly showing your methods.	See pages **vi** and **vii**. Calculations are made to 2dp.
2. Check methods and results to help ensure errors are found and corrected	The student has checked whether her values for mean and standard deviation are sensible in terms of the distribution of the data shown by the bar charts. This is discussed on pages **v** and **vii**. Evidence of checking must be included.
N3.3 Interpret results of your calculations, present your findings and justify your methods. You must use at least one **GRAPH**, one **CHART** and one **DIAGRAM**.	This work includes bar charts (page **iv**) and a frequency table (page **iii**). It therefore has provided evidence of one chart and one diagram. *(A second activity will need to include evidence of use of a graph.)*
Evidence must show you can:	
1. Select appropriate methods of presentation and justify your choice.	This student has drawn computer generated bar charts to display the data on page **iv**. On page **v** there is an explanation of why a bar chart is the most appropriate method to use.
2. Present your findings effectively.	The student has chosen an effective method to display the data. The bar charts are correctly labelled and have suitable headings. On page **v** a written interpretation is given of what the bar charts show in terms of the original purpose.
3. Explain how the results of your calculations relate to the purpose of your activity.	The student has interpreted the results of each of the calculations in terms of the original purpose. These are given on pages **vi** to **vii**. An overall conclusion and interpretation of the work is then given on page **viii**.

Most of the criteria for Level 3 Number have been covered in the newspaper investigation, but Table 4 shows that some further evidence is required for the portfolio. Now look at Table 5, which shows how much evidence this first task has covered.

When planning your portfolio, you need to be efficient in your use of time and energy. **You only need to cover the requirements once, so make sure you cover as much as you can.**

Where's my pen?!

Table 5: How much evidence has the newspaper investigation covered and where is further work needed?

Application of Number portfolio requirements for Level 3	Evidence
N3.1 Plan and interpret information from **TWO** different sources, including a large data set (50+ items).	Source one *Newspaper investigation*
	Source two
	Large data set *Newspaper investigation*
N3.2 Carry out multi-stage calculations to do with: a) amounts and sizes b) scales and proportions c) handling statistics d) rearranging and using formulae You should work with a large data set on at least **ONE** occasion.	A *Newspaper investigation*
	B
	C *Newspaper investigation*
	D *Newspaper investigation*
	Calculations with large set of data *Newspaper investigation*
N3.3 Interpret results of your calculations, present your findings and justify your methods. You must use at least one **GRAPH**, one **CHART** and one **DIAGRAM**.	Graph
	Chart *Newspaper investigation*
	Diagram *Newspaper investigation*

Students doing Maths/Statistics at A Level will find that the coursework required fits very closely with the skills they need to demonstrate for Key Skills Application of Number. However, it is likely there will be work in other subjects that is also a good match to the Key Skills requirements. You could use a logbook to record evidence required for Key Skills that is additional to the evidence required for an assignment.

Looking at the gaps in Table 5, it can be seen that this student now needs to find further evidence of:

- collecting information from another source
- doing calculations involving scales and proportions
- using a graph to display and interpret her data

The student now needs to plan how to cover the remaining portfolio requirements. Are there further opportunities for generating this kind of evidence in the piece of work already undertaken? If not, the student needs to look at her programme of study. It is important to do this **first**.

Ideally you should cover all the evidence requirements in one piece of work. In practice, it has been found that it is extremely difficult to cover all aspects of the evidence requirements for Application of Number in one assignment. It is likely that you will need to consider doing a further piece of work to evidence the remaining skills.

- First, consider whether there are opportunities in your programme of study to generate the evidence you need.

- If there are no further opportunities, make a list of what criteria you still need to cover and think about a second activity you could do. Your teacher may be able to make a few suggestions to help. Don't forget about Enrichment Studies, Duke of Edinburgh or any jobs you have.

KEY POINT

It is not acceptable to use a pre-designed assignment, i.e. one that has been set up for you. The intention is for you to design your own, ideally one that interests you. The Unit Specification states:

'All calculations must be clearly set in context and not be stand-alone exercises.'

Sample portfolio – Activity 2

From Table 5, it is clear this student needs to do a second activity, using a small data sample, involving the use of scales and a graph.

Calculations with scales could involve, for example, drawing plans of a room or using map references to find distance. As part of her Enrichment Studies this student was planning a sponsored walk. She thought that this would give her the remaining evidence required for her portfolio and decided on the following approach to ensure coverage of all remaining portfolio requirements. By doing this, the portfolio for Level 3 Application of Number would consist of only two pieces of work: '**Investigation to show if there is a difference between the length of words in tabloid and broadsheet newspapers**' and '**The Walk**'. No further evidence would be needed.

If you need to do a second activity to meet all the requirements of the Unit Specification, draw up an action plan of what you need to do on similar lines to the following example, making sure that it will provide you with the evidence you require.

Plan for 'The Walk'

N3.1

Plan a walk. Use an OS map to write down grid references and altitudes of points along the route. This will involve collecting information for a small data set.

N3.2

Using the grid references, measure and calculate the distances walked between points, using the map scale and estimate time taken. Calculate overall distance and estimate overall time. These calculations will involve:

- amounts and sizes
- scales and proportions

N3.3

Draw a cross-section of the walk, using distance as the horizontal axis and altitude as the vertical axis. This will represent a graph of the walk. Interpret your graph by writing about how difficult and tiring the walk might be. Write about distances and height climbed on the walk. Will walking uphill and over difficult terrain affect your overall time?

Table 5A shows that all the portfolio requirements have now been met. The student has used only two pieces of work to build her Level 3 portfolio.

Table 5A: Showing how the sample portfolio covers all the evidence required

Application of Number portfolio requirements for Level 3	Evidence
N3.1 Plan and interpret information from **TWO** different sources, including a large data set (50+ items).	Source one Newspaper investigation
	Source two The Walk
	Large data set Newspaper investigation
N3.2 Carry out multi-stage calculations to do with: a) amounts and sizes b) scales and proportions c) handling statistics d) rearranging and using formulae You should work with a large data set on at least **ONE** occasion.	A Newspaper investigation
	B The Walk
	C Newspaper investigation
	D Newspaper investigation
	Calculations with large set of data Newspaper investigation
N3.3 Interpret results of your calculations, present your findings and justify your methods. You must use at least one **GRAPH**, one **CHART** and one **DIAGRAM**.	Graph The Walk
	Chart Newspaper investigation
	Diagram Newspaper investigation

TIP

Where appropriate, include the assignment brief and your teacher's assessment of the work in the subject. This evidence is vital to the Key Skills assessor and moderator. He or she will need to understand what you were asked to do, and have an appreciation of the quality and standard of your work in terms of subject content.

Suggestions for a major piece of evidence

If the subjects you study do not offer many opportunities for generating evidence for Application of Number, you need to design a piece of work for yourself. This is not as hard as it sounds! It's always better to work on something that interests you. Look at the sample portfolio and at Table 2 in Chapter 6 to help you think about what the work you do must cover. You can do anything you like but you need to find a task that would:

● involve collecting a large data set of 50+ items

● cover as many of the different types of calculation for N3.2

● involve drawing and interpreting graphs, diagrams or charts for N3.3

Opportunities for a major piece of evidence

If you look on the website for EDEXCEL (www.edexcel.org.uk), one of the major awarding bodies, you will find a grid showing the development and assessment opportunities within each Advanced GCE subject.

The only subjects that show no opportunities within their specification for Application of Number are listed as:

    Art & Design
    English Literature, English Language and English Literature & Language
    History
    Modern Foreign Languages
    Music
    Religious Studies

However, this book has already demonstrated how a piece of coursework for an English Language qualification could include number evidence, and the same could be done with all of the subjects above with some careful thought and planning.

Enrichment Studies

These are often a good opportunity to evidence Application of Number. Are you doing community or charity work? Are you learning to drive? Think about a project you could undertake which involves collecting numerical data and working with number.

Employment

Do you have a part-time job, perhaps in the retail sector? How does the weather or the time of the year affect sales? Could you develop a project along these lines investigating trends?

Advanced VEC Travel & Tourism

Could you investigate the growth in foreign travel? Why do airlines needs more runways/more capacity? Could this growth be satisfied with larger aircraft carrying more passengers?

TIP

Obviously, it is not intended that you copy these ideas but they do illustrate just how easy it can be to generate Application of Number evidence from subjects or programmes which at first glance seem to have little to do with number. If you understand what the Unit Specification requires, you can produce evidence from a wide range of programmes or activities in which you are already involved. It just takes a bit of thought!

Other sources of information

The Internet. There are good sources of data on the Internet. You could try the Office for National Statistics Stats Base website, www.ons.gov.uk. Can you find any data of interest to you there? Remember that you need a large set of unprocessed data.

CD-ROMs are another source. 'Secos', Statistics for Education, is a useful source of data and should be available in most libraries.

Reference books are another source you could use. The following texts have plentiful sources of data.

- 'The Economist' Book of Vital World Statistics

- Philip's Geographical Digest

- Social Trends, a government publication. Be careful to choose a topic with a large data base.

Once you have decided what you will do, make a plan of your approach, taking into account the advice given in Chapters 6, 7 and 8 on what to include in your written report. Try to be imaginative in your approach to cover as many of the portfolio requirements as possible.

To sum up

- Once you have completed a substantial piece of work, on the lines of the newspaper investigation example in this book, you need to check the portfolio requirements for further evidence.

- Fill in Table 2 in Chapter 6 (there is another copy in Appendix D on page 77) to see where you need to do further work for your portfolio.

- Make a list of what you need to cover and try to design a task you could do that covers all criteria for N3.1, 3.2 and 3.3 as well as fulfilling the remaining portfolio requirements.

- Look at the advice on planning 'The Walk' in Chapter 8 to help you.

You should now be ready to start your portfolio planning – GOOD LUCK!

Appendices

A Application of Number Level 3 – Unit Specification

B Answers to practice questions (Chapter 4)

C Answers to Exemplar Test (Chapter 5)

D Contents of a Level 3 Application of Number Portfolio (Table 2)

E Proxy Qualifications

F Where to find out more

KEY SKILLS UNIT

Application of number

What is this unit about?

This unit is about applying your number skills in a substantial and complex activity.

You will show you can:

- plan, and interpret information from different sources;

- carry out multi-stage calculations;

- present findings, explain results and justify your choice of methods.

How do I use the information in this unit?

The unit has three parts: what you need to know, what you must do and guidance.

Part **A**
WHAT YOU NEED TO KNOW

This part of the unit tells you what you need to learn and practise to feel confident about applying number skills in your studies, work or other aspects of your life.

Part **B**
WHAT YOU MUST DO

This part of the unit describes the skills you must show. All your work for this section will be assessed. You must have evidence that you can do all the things listed in the bullet points.

Part **C**
GUIDANCE

This part describes some activities you might like to use to develop and show your number skills. It also contains examples of the sort of evidence you could produce to prove you have the skills required.

LEVEL 3

Part A

WHAT YOU NEED TO KNOW

In planning an activity and interpreting information,

YOU NEED TO KNOW HOW TO:

- plan a substantial and complex activity by breaking it down into a series of tasks;

- obtain relevant information from different sources, including a large data set (over 50 items), and use this to meet the purpose of your activity;

- use estimation to help you plan, multiplying and dividing numbers of any size rounded to one significant figure;

- make accurate and reliable observations over time and use suitable equipment to measure in a variety of appropriate units;

- read and understand scale drawings, graphs, complex tables and charts;

- read and understand ways of writing very large and very small numbers *(eg £1.5 billion, 2.4x10⁻³)*;

- understand and use compound measures *(eg speed in kph, pressures in psi, concentrations in ppm)*;

- choose appropriate methods for obtaining the results you need and justify your choice.

In carrying out calculations,

YOU NEED TO KNOW HOW TO:

- show your methods clearly and work to appropriate levels of accuracy;

- carry out multi-stage calculations with numbers of any size *(eg find the results of growth at 8% over three years, find the volume of water in a swimming pool)*;

- use powers and roots *(eg work out interest on £5,000 at 5% over three years)*;

- work out missing angles and sides in right-angled triangles from known sides and angles;

- work out proportional change *(eg add VAT at 17.5% by multiplying by 1.175)*;

- work out actual measurements from scale drawings *(eg room or site plan, map, workshop drawing)* and scale quantities up and down;

- work with large data sets (over 50 items), using measures of average and range to compare distributions, and estimate mean, median and range of grouped data;

- re-arrange and use formulae, equations and expressions *(eg formulae in spreadsheets, finance, and area and volume calculations)*;

- use checking procedures to identify errors in methods and results.

In interpreting results and presenting your findings,

YOU NEED TO KNOW HOW TO:

- select and use appropriate methods to illustrate findings, show trends and make comparisons;

- examine critically, and justify, your choice of methods;

- construct and label charts, graphs, diagrams and scale drawings using accepted conventions;

- draw appropriate conclusions based on your findings, including how possible sources of error might have affected your results;

- explain how your results relate to the purpose of your activity.

Part B

WHAT YOU MUST DO

You must:

Plan and carry through at least one substantial and complex activity that includes tasks for N3.1, N3.2 and N3.3

N3.1

Plan, and interpret information from **two** different types of sources, including a large data set.

Evidence must show you can:

- plan how to obtain and use the information required to meet the purpose of your activity;
- obtain the relevant information; and
- choose appropriate methods for obtaining the results you need and justify your choice.

N3.2

Carry out multi-stage calculations to do with:

    a amounts and sizes;

    b scales and proportion;

    c handling statistics;

    d rearranging and using formulae.

You should work with a large data set on at least **one** occasion.

- carry out calculations to appropriate levels of accuracy, clearly showing your methods; and
- check methods and results to help ensure errors are found and corrected.

N3.3

Interpret results of your calculations, present your findings and justify your methods. You must use at least **one** graph, **one** chart and **one** diagram.

- select appropriate methods of presentation and justify your choice;
- present your findings effectively; and
- explain how the results of your calculations relate to the purpose of your activity.

Part C

GUIDANCE

Examples of activities you might use

You will have opportunities to develop and apply your number skills during your work, studies or other activities. For example, when:

- planning, carrying out and reporting findings from a substantial investigation or project;
- designing, making and presenting a product;
- researching information and explaining the outcomes to customers or clients.

You will need time to practise your skills and prepare for assessment. So it is important to plan ahead. For example, to identify an activity that is complex and substantial enough to provide opportunities for following through tasks for N3.1, N3.2 and N3.3. You may need to do additional tasks to cover all the requirements of Part B.

Information can be obtained from secondary sources and/or first-hand by measuring or observing. If available, you could use IT to obtain information from a large database, use spreadsheets and present your findings.

This unit is for use in programmes starting from September 2000.

QCA/99/342   First published 1999

Copyright © 1999 Qualifications and Curriculum Authority.

Reproduction, storage, adaption or translation, in any form or by any means, of this publication is prohibited without prior written permission of the publisher, or within the terms of licences issued by the Copyright Licensing Agency. Excerpts may be reproduced for the purpose of research, private study, criticism or review, or by educational institutions solely for educational purposes, without permission, providing full acknowledgement is given.

Printed in Great Britain.

The Qualifications and Curriculum Authority is an exempt charity under the Charities Act 1960.

Qualifications and Curriculum Authority, 29 Bolton Street, London W1Y 7PD. www.qca.org.uk   Chairman: Sir William Stubbs.

Copies of this document may be obtained using the QCA *Publications List and Order Form* or by contacting: QCA Publications, PO Box 99, Sudbury, Suffolk, CO10 6SN. Telephone: 01787 884444, Fax: 01787 378426. When ordering, please quote title and reference number.

QCA

CCEA

ACCAC

You will need to think about the quality of your application of number skills and check your evidence covers all the requirements in Part B.

Examples of evidence

3.1 PLAN, AND INTERPRET INFORMATION

A description of the substantial and complex activity and tasks. A plan for obtaining and using the information required.

Copies of source material, including a note of the large data set and, if applicable, a statement from someone who has checked the accuracy of any measurements or observations.

Records of the information obtained. A justification of methods selected for achieving the required results.

3.2 CARRY OUT CALCULATIONS

Records of your calculations (for a, b, c and d), showing methods used and levels of accuracy.

Notes of the large data set used and how you checked methods and results.

3.3 INTERPRET RESULTS AND PRESENT FINDINGS

Report of your findings, including a justification of your presentation methods and explanations of how your results relate to your activity. At least one graph, one chart and one diagram.

If producing certain types of evidence creates difficulties, due to disability or other factors, you may be able to use other ways to show your achievement. Ask your tutor or superviser for further information.

Part I – Questions to practise number skills

1 £2166.67

2 48

3 1/8

4 a) 2/15   b) 5625

5 143

6 30%

7 42

8 £12.25

9 7 litres

10 50:20:30 days

11 2:1

12 a) £100

   b) 500 miles

   c) Cost = £25 + 0.25x

13 a) 60 mph

   b) D = Speed × Time

   c) 200 miles

14 a) 36,300 pesetas

   b) £ = P/242

15 a) 314 cm²

   b) 62.8 cm

16 £55

17 −15 °C

18 a) £132,400,000

   b) £130,000,000

19 a) sixty million, two hundred and fifty four thousand, three hundred

   b) 6.03×10^7

   c) 3,020,042

   d) 3,020,000

20 a) 4.3×10^4

   b) 5.8×10^7

   c) 1.2×10^{-5}

   d) 2,480,000

   e) 0.000 002 48

21 a) 71 m²

   b) 36 m

   c) 163.3 m³

   d) 23 cm

22 15.7 litres

23 mean = £8.00

   median = £7.50

   mode = £7.50

   range = £5.70

24 cones = 80p, choc-ices = 90p

25 man's age 45, son is 3

26 let CDs be x and tapes be y

   $10x + 6y \leq 150$

   $x \leq 12, y \leq 9$

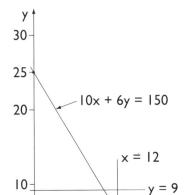

Look for whole number points in shaded region.

Possible answers:

CD's	tapes
9	9
10	8
11	6
12	5

27 7.9 cm

28 11.9 cm

29 8.4 cm

30 6.8 cm

31 71.6°

1 £200

2 a) 4,050   b) 2,952

3 a) 600 g   b) 450 g

4 a) 100 m^2 b) 1.46 cm

5 7.5 × 16 × 30.5 = 3,660 cm^3; setting should be 3,600 cm^3 (to nearest 100)

6 A box contains 40 oranges whose weights are shown in the following frequency table:

Weight (g)	70	80	90	100	110	120	Total
Frequency	2	6	10	11	7	4	40
Cumulative frequency	2	8	18	29	36	40	
weight × frequency	140	480	900	1,100	770	480	3,870

Use this information to calculate the

a) mean = 3870/40 = 96.75 = 97g

b) Use cumulative frequency, median = 100g

c) mode = 100g

d) range = 120 – 70 = 50g

7 A factory has 400 employees who are paid by the hour at the following rates:

Hourly wage in pence mid value	£3.50	£4.50	£5.50	£6.50	£7.50	£8.50
No. of workers	10	25	134	85	69	77
f × mid value	£35	£112.5	£737	£552.50	£517.5	£654.50
Cumulative f	10	35	169	254	323	400

a) mean = £2609/ 400 = £6.52 nearest p
   median = £6.50
   mode = £5.50

b) The data is skewed, so better to use median rather than mean

8 Amanda wants to check she is getting good mileage from the fuel she uses in her car. She uses the following table to record her calculations.

	miles at start	miles at end	total miles	no. of litres of petrol	cost per litre	miles per litre	cost per mile
Journey 1	53478	53,724	246	30	86.4p	8.2	10.54p
Journey 2	53724	54276	552	60	88.2p	9.2	9.6

a) The mileage at the end of the journey – 53724

b) The rate in miles per litre – 246/30 = 8.2 miles per litre

c) The cost per mile – 60 × 88.2 = 5292p, 5292/552 = 9.58695 = 9.6p per mile

9 'Cut-Price' sells glass cut to any size. The recommended safety thickness and the cost depend on the area of glass sold. This information is given in the table below.

Area of glass (m^2)	Safety thickness (mm)	Cost per m^2
up to $1m^2$	3	£8.50
$1m^2$ up to $2.5m^2$	4	£17.50
$2.5m^2$ up to $9m^2$	6	£27.50
$9m^2$ up to $22m^2$	12	£97.00

a) 46×50 by 34×50 mm = 2300×1700 mm = 2.3×1.7 m = 3.91 m^2. Use 6 mm thick glass.

b) $3 \times 1 = 3$ m^2. Use 6 mm thick glass. Estimated cost = $4 \times 3 = 12$ m^2, $12 \times 30 = £360$.

c) $2.65 \times 0.55 = 1.4575$ m^2. Use 4 mm glass. $1.4575 \times £17.50 = £25.50625$, by 4 panes = £102.025 = £102.03, about one third the estimated cost , which is a long way out.

d) Rounding to 2sf, $2.7 \times 0.6 = 1.62$ m^2. Use 4 mm glass. $1.6 \times £18 = £28.80$, approx. £29, $\times$ 4 panes = £116, which is much closer to the real cost.

10 The figures in the following table relate to the amount of bottled water consumed in four different countries in 1998.

Table A: Bottled Water Consumption in 1998

Country	France	Germany	US	UK
Population size	57,289,000	80,293,000	255,414,000	58,144,000
Total amount in £s paid for bottled water by population (1998)	1.374936×10^9	1.686153×10^9	2.043312×10^9	4.6512×10^8
Average consumption per head (volume in litres)	114	72	17	13
Answer a)	$57,289,000 \times 114 = 6,530,946,000$	$80,293,000 \times 72 = 5,781,096,000$	$255,414,000 \times 17 = 4,342,038,000$	$58,144,000 \times 13 = 755,872,000$
Answer b)	$1.374936 \times 10^9 \div 6530946000 = £0.2105 = 21p$	$1.686153 \times 10^9 \div 5781096000 = 29p$	$2.043312 \times 10^9 \div 4342038000 = 47p$	$4.6512 \times 10^8 \div 755872000 = 62p$
Answer c)	France is cheapest			UK most expensive
Answer d) cost 1998 per person	$114 \times 0.21 = £23.94$	$72 \times 0.29 = £20.88$	$17 \times 0.47 = £7.99$	$13 \times 0.62 = £8.06$
Average amount paid in £s per person for bottled water (1994)	£22.86	£22.36	£6.78	£6.72
difference	£1.08	−£1.48	£1.21	£1.34
Answer e) % change	£1.08/22.86 × 100 = 4.7%	−£1.48/22.36 × 100 = −6.6%	£1.21/6.78 × 100 = 17.8%	£1.34/6.72 × 100 = 19.9%

f) The price of bottled water has dropped in Germany, while the largest increase in price has been in the UK.

g) Tap water costs 6.2×10^{-2} pence per litre = 0.062p

From part b) bottled water costs 62p, $0.062 \times 1000 = 62$. The price of bottled water is 1000 times more expensive than tap water.

11 a) APR = $100((1 + (0.01)(0.9))^{12} - 1)$
  = $100(1.009^{12} - 1)$
  = $100(1.1135 - 1)$
  = $100(0.1135)$
  = 11.35%

b) Sure Savers £3300

Technology £3000 $\times (1.009)^{12}$ = £3340.53

He should use the Technology Bank. His savings will be worth £40.53 more after a year there.

12 Harry owns 250 acres of farmland in Sussex. The government is planning to build large numbers of new houses and he can gain planning permission to build houses on 56 acres of his land. When he bought his land in the 1960s it was worth £200,000. In the year 2000, agricultural land is valued at £2500 per acre.

Using 0.4047 acres = 1 hectare and 100 hectares = 1 km^2

a) 250/0.4047 = 617.741 hectares, 617.741/100 = 6.177 = 6.2 km^2

b) 250×2500 = £625000

c) increase = £425000, % increase = $425000/200000 \times 100$ = 212.5%

d) £2500 : £750000 = 1 : 300. Land for houses is worth 300 times the value of agricultural land.

e) solely agricultural land = £625000

56 acres houses = $56 \times 750,000$ = £42,000,000
250 − 56 = 194, 194×2500 = £485,000
Value with 56 acres for houses = £42,485,000

Ratio 625,000 : 42,485,000 = 625 : 42,485 = 125 : 8,497, approximately 1 : 68
With planning permission for houses the land would be worth 68 times more than if solely used for agriculture.

f) check result for e) $68 \times 625,000$ = £42,500,000, which is very close to answer in part e).

13 a)

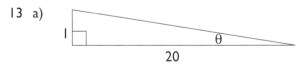

tan θ = 1/20 = 0.05, angle of elevation = inv tan 0.05 = 2.86°

b)

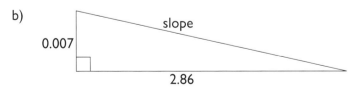

sin 2.86° = 0.007/slope, slope = 0.007/sin 2.86° = 0.14029 = 0.140m

c) Check – use Pythagoras: slope = $\sqrt{(1^2 + 20^2)} = \sqrt{401}$ = 20.02498
1 unit on plan = 0.007m, slope = 20.02498×0.007 = 0.140m, giving the same answer as before.

14 a)

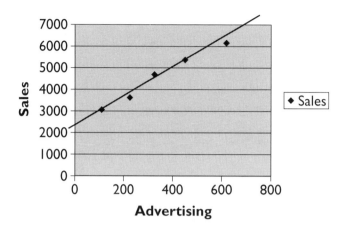

Scatter graph to show impact of advertising on sales

b) Draw a straight line as close to all the points as you can.

c) The graph shows a positive correlation between amount spent on advertising and sales. It shows that spending on advertising has increased sales.

d) Approximately £550

1 For simplified calculation such as
   $700 \div (40 \times 0.5)$ *1 mark*
   results between 35 and 40   *1 mark*
                                           Total 2 marks

2 a) Accept values between 4.4 m and 4.72 m
                                                 1 mark

   b) area of garage door = $3.8 \times 0.8 \times 3.3 \times 0.8$
      $= 8.03 \text{ m}^2$

      accept values between 7.55 m^2 and 8.52 m^2
                                                 1 mark

   c) rectangle measures 7.5 cm $\pm$ 1 mm by
      5.8 cm $\pm$ 1 mm   *1 mark*
                                           Total 3 marks

3
Ingredients	number of filled rolls	Amount of ingredient needed for rolls requested
Butter 1 kg	200	0.54 kg
Tomatoes 1 kg	25	4.32 kg
Ham 1 kg	20	2.50 kg
Cheese 1 kg	30	0.67 kg
Tuna 1 tin	10	4 tins
Lettuce 1	15	8 lettuces

Clear table (such as one above) with correct
list of quantities required.   *3 marks*

List of quantities with at least 5 correct
amounts   *(1 mark)*

List of quantities with at least 3 correct
amounts   *(1 mark)*
                                           Total 3 marks

4 a) Trials and improvement or by testing various
      values of n in an equation such as $1.045^n = 2$
      leads to $1.045^{15} = 1.94$, while $1.045^{16} = 2.022$,
      so population will have doubled within 16 years.
      For 16 years   *2 marks*
      For 15 years   *(1 mark)*

   b) Forecast depends on existing circumstances
      being maintained. Factors which could affect
      the forecast include

        reduction in life expectancy

        increased net emigration

        reduction in family sizes

        later commencement of families

        for any one such appropriate statement
                                                 1 mark
                                           Total 3 marks

5 a) mean number of children = 2.16   *2 marks*
      for calculation which includes a total number
      of children divided by 50   *(1 mark)*

   b) There will be a higher number of families
      with 3 or more children   *1 mark*
      Mode is 1 (lower than in first group of
      families), but mean number of children is
      higher than in first group of families. There
      must be a larger number of families with 3
      and over children to produce the higher
      mean.   *1 mark*
                                           Total 4 marks

6 tables cost £63.00 each,
   so total VAT reclaimed = 17.5/117.5 of table
   cost which gives £140.74   *2 marks*
   for calculation of price per table without VAT,
   of £53.62   *(1 mark)*
                                           Total 2 marks

7 a) amount of chlorine = 7.2 gallons =
      32.76 litres.   *1 mark*

   b) total volume of water required =
      $21 \times 15.6 \times 1.5 = 491.4 \text{ m}^3$
      = 491 000 litres
      = 108 000 gallons
      so extra water required =
      18 000 gallons   *2 marks*
      for volume of water of 491.4 m^3 *(1 mark)*
                                           Total 3 marks

8 a) flour 450 grams, baking powder 37.5 grams
                                            1 mark each

   b) baking time is 3.3 hours or about 3 hours
      20 minutes
      for any time between 3.2 hours
      and 3.35 hours   *1 mark*

   c) if F is 350 then C is 176.67
      for 177°   *(1 mark)*
      for 175° or 180°   *2 marks*
                                           Total 5 marks

9 a) 0.86, 1.00, 0.77, 1.00, 1.00, 0.81   *3 marks*
      at least 2 correct   *(1 mark)*
      at least 4 correct   *(2 marks)*
      clear indication of method of calculation for
      at least one H value   *1 mark*

   b) group A range = 0.14, group B range = 0.23
      for both correct   *1 mark*
      (allow follow through from part a)

A mean = 0.94, B mean = 0.91 *1 mark each*

(Alternatively A median = 0.97,
B median = 0.93) *(1 mark)*

Explanation of average calculation (for mean or median) *1 mark*

Explanation such as: mean better choice than median, because median depends only on middle two results. *1 mark*

c) Possible comparison points include

  H values for group B more spread out than for group A

  On average, group B less fit than group A

For two or more valid points *2 marks*

For one valid point *(1 mark)*

d)

Person	H	BMI
G	0.97	18
H	0.84	26
J	0.98	26
K	0.98	23
L	0.93	26
M	0.86	19
N	1.00	20
P	0.77	17
Q	1.00	19
R	1.00	22
S	0.81	27

For all 11 BMIs correct *3 marks*

For 10 correct *(2 marks)*

For 9 correct *(1 mark)*

For clear table, at least including information shown above *1 mark*

(allow follow through from wrongly calculated H values)

e) choice of scatter graph *1 mark*

title for graph *1 mark*

sensible choice of scales *1 mark*

labels *1 mark*

11 points plotted clearly and accurately from table in part d *3 marks*

10 points plotted *(2 marks)*

9 points plotted *(1 mark)*

f) Points include

scatter of points shows not possible to estimate fitness from BMI

lower H values occur with extreme BMI values of 19, 25 and 27

too small a sample to draw any conclusions

fitness influenced by other factors (exercise, training) as well as BMI

some very fit very muscular people will have high BMIs

for three valid comments *3 marks*

for two valid comments *(2 marks)*

for one valid comment *(1 mark)*

Total 25 marks

Total for paper 50 marks

D Contents of a Level 3 Application of Number Portfolio (Table 2)

Application of Number portfolio requirements for Level 3	Evidence
N3.1 Plan and interpret information from **TWO** different sources, including a large data set (50+ items).	Source one
	Source two
	Large data set
N3.2 Carry out multi-stage calculations to do with: a) amounts and sizes b) scales and proportions c) handling statistics d) rearranging and using formulae You should work with a large data set on at least **ONE** occasion.	A
	B
	C
	D
	Calculations with large set of data
N3.3 Interpret results of your calculations, present your findings and justify your methods. You must use at least one **GRAPH**, one **CHART** and one **DIAGRAM**.	Graph
	Chart
	Diagram

E Proxy Qualifications

Details of proxy qualifications to act as exemptions from parts of the Key Skills Qualification. Parts A and B apply.

Part A (External Assessment)

English Language or Literature, Gaelic and Welsh, and Communication

Mathematics[1] and Application of Number

> GCE AS/A Level A-E examination performance provides exemption for the external test in these Key Skills at Level 3.
>
> GCSE A*-C examination performance provides exemption for the external test in these Key Skills at Level 2.
>
> GCSE D-G examination performance provides exemption for the external test in these Key Skills at Level 1.

Computing[1] or ICT[1] and Information Technology

> GCE A Level A-E performance provides full exemption for the Key Skill at Level 3.
>
> GCE AS A-E performance provides exemption for the external test in the Key Skill at Level 3.
>
> GCSE A*-C performance provides full exemption for the Key Skill at Level 2.
>
> GCSE D-G performance provides full exemption for the Key Skill at Level 1.

GCSE Short Course ICT[1] and Information Technology

> A*-C performance provides exemption for the external test in the Key Skill at Level 2 and also for one of the two specified purposes of the internal Key Skill component at Level 2.
>
> D-G performance provides exemption for the external test in the Key Skill at Level 1 and also for one of the two specified purposes of the internal Key Skill component at Level 1.

Part Award, Single Award or Double Award in Vocational A Level and GNVQ or Part One GNVQ in ICT[1] and Information Technology

> Vocational AS/A Level (Advanced GNVQ) A-E performance provides full exemption for the Key Skill at Level 3.
>
> Intermediate GNVQ or Part One GNVQ Pass/Merit/Distinction performance provides full exemption for the Key Skill at Level 2.
>
> Foundation GNVQ or Part One GNVQ Pass/Merit/Distinction performance provides full exemption for the Key Skill at Level 1.

The currency of qualification specifications

> The above exemptions have been confirmed for those specifications accredited by the regulatory authorities. Revision to accredited specifications would result in the exemptions offered by that subject being reviewed and if necessary revised or removed.

The currency of examination performance

> The currency of exemptions provided by proxy qualifications must be no longer than three years from the date of award to the date of claim. In these circumstances, exemptions from September 2000 can only be claimed for qualifications gained after September 1997.

[1] This applies to all qualifications whether gained through the medium of English, Gaelic or Welsh

Part B (Portfolio)

NATIONAL QUALIFICATIONS FRAMEWORK

The following titles for English, Mathematics and ICT Qualifications provide exemptions to the external assessment of the Key Skills.

For the Communication Key Skill

ENGLISH

GCSE English

GCSE English Literature

GCE AS and Advanced English Language

GCE AS and Advanced English Language and Literature

For the Application of Number Key Skill

MATHEMATICS

GCSE Mathematics

GCE AS or GCE Advanced Mathematics

GCE AS or GCE Advanced Pure Mathematics

GCE AS or GCE Advanced Further Mathematics

GCE AS or GCE Advanced Statistics

GCE AS Mechanics

GCE AS Discrete Mathematics

GCE AS Applied Mathematics

For the IT Key Skill

ICT

GCSE IT

GCSE (Short Course) ICT

GCE AS ICT

GCE AS Computing

GCE A ICT

GCE A Computing

GNVQ Foundation ICT (6-unit award)

GNVQ Foundation ICT (3-unit award)

GNVQ Intermediate ICT (6-unit award)

GNVQ Intermediate ICT (3-unit award

GNVQ Advanced ICT (12-unit award)

GNVQ Advanced ICT (6-unit award)

GNVQ Advanced ICT (3-unit award)

F   Where to find out more

Useful websites

Association of Colleges (AoC)
www.aoc.co.uk

BBC Further Education
www.bbc.co.uk/education/fe
www.bbc.co.uk/education/fe/skills/index.shtml

Department for Education and Employment
www.dfee.gov.uk
If you are involved in producing a Progress File you can gain help from
www.dfee.gov.uk/progfile/index.htm

Further Education Development Agency (FEDA) – the main body leading Key
Skills developments in schools and colleges.
www.feda.ac.uk

For **GNVQ support** try
www.feda.ac.uk/gnvq

National Extension College (NEC) – produces useful material to support Key
Skills development.
www.nec.ac.uk/index.html

Qualifications and Curriculum Authority (QCA) – the organisation
responsible for the development, implementation and quality assurance of all national
qualifications.
www.qca.org.uk

University and Colleges Admissions Service (UCAS)
www.ucas.ac.uk

Letts Educational
www.letts–education.com